DOG TALES

NIGEL HEMMING

I first met Nigel in 1985. At that time he was painting watercolour portraits of peoples' dogs and cats, commissioned through the Halcyon Gallery. The following year we launched the Washington Green Fine Art Publishing Company with four dogs, four ducks, four game birds and four hunt scenes created by Nigel. This series of sporting images were based on a central watercolour study surrounded by pencil vignettes. These became one of the most successful ranges we have ever published and are still in print today with sales totalling well in excess of one hundred thousand prints throughout Europe and the US. Following this, Nigel went on to develop his own technique and style through the medium of acrylic and then to oils.

Nigel's ability to create a narrative picture and at the same time to capture the charm and endearing qualities of his subject has made him the country's favourite painter of canine imagery and now his limited edition prints are much sought after and highly collectable. In 1994 Nigel was commissioned by the Franklin Mint to produce a series of collector plates. This collaboration proved to be extremely successful. He is currently completing his sixth series for the Mint and again, has gone on to be one of their most collected artists selling through some 37 countries world-wide.

Nigel is a great believer in supporting the animals he so dearly loves and which through their different characters and nature have inspired him to create the narrative images for which he is now best known. Nigel has been involved in creating various projects for different animal charities including his endearing portrayal of the puppies in "Guiding Lights" to raise money for Guide Dogs for the Blind.

Over the years, Nigel and myself have enjoyed a warm friendship as well as a great working relationship and because of this, we are very proud to publish this long awaited book which brings together the stories behind the pictures. I hope that this book gives you much pleasure.

Glyn Washington.

First Published in Great Britain in 1997 by Washington Green (FAPC) Limited
30 Marshall Street, Birmingham B1 1LE
Illustrations and Text © Washington Green/Nigel Hemming
Designed by Jonathan Kearns

British Library Cataloguing in Publication Data
Nigel Hemming - Dog Tales
ISBN 0 9525833 6 4

WASHINGTON GREEN PUBLICATIONS

To Sue, who has made it all possible
And in loving memory of Pete
(21.5.1960 – 11.2.1997)

Nigel Hemming is undoubtedly one of the country's most successful animal artists. Born in 1957 in Staffordshire, his career has been well documented with transition through the media of watercolour, acrylic, pastel, and finally oil.

Although he initially saw himself as a wildlife artist - ornithological subjects holding a particular fascination for him - it is the painting of dogs - particularly working dogs - with which his name has become associated. The relationship between man and dog provides an endless source of inspiration for his work.

Living with his own dogs has made Nigel a keen observer of canine behaviour and his images reflect this deep understanding of his subject.

Devotees find his paintings irresistible - seeing many of their own special animal's endearing traits captured on canvas.

Nigel's work has been published in limited edition form since the mid 1980's, enjoying increasing popularity with each new edition. His published works and original paintings have featured in one- man shows as well as a number of shared exhibitions. His work is collected throughout the U.K., Europe and U.S.A.

In 1996 Nigel received the Fine Art Trade Guilds published 'Artist of the Year' award.

Introduction

IDEAS ARE EVERYTHING!

This is, of course, a rather sweeping statement and perhaps a slight exaggeration as it implies that the technical side of things - the actual application of paint by brush to canvas - is relatively unimportant. However, the creation of narrative within a painting, or at least the feeling that something has, or is just about to happen, remains at the very heart of my continued excitement and fascination with painting.

There are simply no parameters to govern the origins of ideas. A chance comment, common sayings or expressions, even the lyrics of a song can be a source of inspiration, but by far and away the most important factor is the power of observation.

My Art teacher at school, Peter Mansell, always said that to capture the essence of something on paper requires ninety per cent looking and ten per cent drawing. It's a golden rule that applies across the board. Unless you take time to know and understand your subject, you'll never be able to interpret and fully express what it is you want to say about it. From time to time Peter would tell the class to take off a shoe and draw it. Not the most exciting of exercises I admit, however, it made us look closely at objects which we all took for granted, objects with which we were familiar as a result of daily use and had looked at many times, yet never really seen.

I'd been painting dogs professionally for nearly five years, when I met and married my wife Sue, (a serious dog and cat lover.) Up to that point, I had no first hand experience of living with dogs. Sue had an ageing Sheltie named Micky and an old tabby called Sherry when we met and it was into all of their lives that I somehow had to fit. It was an experience both pleasant and trying - probably as much for the animals as for myself. Nevertheless, for me, it was the beginning of a wonderful and fascinating learning curve.

Prior to my marriage, my paintings of dogs had not strayed far from simple one-off watercolour portraits of people's pets. Although I had enjoyed a modicum of success doing this it was a combination of three factors that I feel marked the turning point in my career. My professional relationship with Paul Green and The Halcyon Gallery in Birmingham was the first. In time this led to my acquaintance and subsequent association with Glyn Washington and Washington Green Fine Art Publishing Company. I was both fortunate and privileged to be involved with both of these companies from their early days and feel that, in some ways, we have grown up together. The third factor was my marriage to Sue which, in itself, has been the most wonderfully satisfying (and indeed stabilizing) influence on my life. As part of that whole experience came the added bonus of living with dogs.

Two years into our marriage, with old Mick's days obviously numbered, Sue and I decided the time had come to acquire a new puppy. As it turned out we ended up with two - Jessie and Martha - cross-collie-litter-sisters and the biggest single influence on my painting to date.

In 1988 I painted my first narrative piece - a picture entitled "In Retirement."(cover and page 91) It was an idea that I had been mulling over for several years prior to actually commencing painting. It has also proved, coincidentally, to be one of the most popular images that I have ever produced. It's a concept I feel sure would never have evolved without the insights that I have gained from sharing my life with dogs.

As I said at the beginning, observation is the most vital ingredient when it comes to painting and from that point of view living with dogs has been a revelation to me. There is another factor which I have not yet mentioned and which is undoubtedly of equal importance. It is an element that is indefinable and totally abstract. It is an all-important quality which most artists find invaluable. And what is this strange and magical ingredient? Imagination!

In the spring of 1995, it occurred to me that, as I was the painter of narrative pictures, a natural progression would be to write stories which went with my images. The first of these was "Wish You Were Here" (page 79). Even allowing for the fact that new ideas sometimes take time to catch on, the concept seemed to be quite successful.

Producing the story on a separate sheet from the print gave people the choice of either retaining it with the print, shoving it in a drawer and forgetting all about it, or even disposing of it completely.

Apart from providing me with an alternative way of expressing my ideas, it also proved to be the tentative beginnings of a genre which ultimately evolved into this book.

It is a collection of verse, stories, (both true and fictional) all of which are about or inspired by selected pictures that I have painted over the past ten years. I hope that there is something for everyone, and that even people who are not really "into" dogs find something within these pages to give them pleasure.

Contents

The Tales....

Like Father Like Son

"It's a very important business being a dog; especially if you're a working dog and particularly if you're a Labrador." That's what my dad always says anyway. "Son," he'll say, "We Labradors, like all dogs, have loyalties. First and foremost, to the master of course. We are not, however, the same as all dogs. We have status - a position - we have importance! The master will expect much of you and quite rightly too. He'll put considerable time and effort into your training. You'll learn, on his command, to sit and stay, to come when called, and also to walk at heel. But perhaps most importantly, you'll learn how to retrieve. This is the task most fundamental to our illustrious breed.

All of these are primary responsibilities to our position as the master's chief steward. There are, however, allegiances that, as a Labrador, you are duty bound to observe and adhere to.

When you are with the master, in the field or simply walking, never forget what you are. It is not enough to obey well the master's every command - to go when you are sent and to come when called - it is equally important to be seen to be doing it well. When in the field, you must be especially mindful of your status. There will be many other dogs with their masters. Springer Spaniels - Golden Retrievers - Setters and Pointers - all fine breeds, with many good points. There are, of course, also, those wretched, cheeky and disrespectful Terriers. You'll be advised to stay well away from them. You may even come across the occasional Yellow Labrador. Don't be deceived by the fact that they go by the name Labrador. They are simply a tragic genetic aberration which only exist thanks to the misguided attitudes of certain humans. I'm sure that they're decent enough fellows, but remember, the only true colour is black." Yes! My dad is a very important dog. A fact reflected in the respect shown to him by all the animals on the estate.

There's only one person that seems to hold my father in less than the highest regard and that's my mother; at least that's the impression I was under until recently. You see, just the other day I happened to overhear a conversation between my mom and Martha, the Collie from next door. They were apparently talking about my father and I heard my mom say to Martha that my dad was, "A pompous old wind-bag." I didn't know what it meant but judging from their meaningful nods and knowing smiles, it must be very important. When I grow up, I want to be a "Pompous old wind-bag," just like my dad. I know that training and status are very important and of course, I want my father to be proud of me, but, let's face it, I'm a six week old puppy. What do I care about sitting around in fields, fetching and carrying to command and especially what other dogs think of me? I want to be off - playing "Bite the Puppy's Tail," or "Chasing the Chickens" in the yard. (That's a great game, but you have to be really quick on your feet. Some of those hens pack a mean peck.) There's also, "Explore the Barn." I really love that game because, when I've delved to the deepest, darkest corners, fighting my way through marauding mice - when I've scaled the steps to the heights of the loft and stand alone at the top of the world, I usually feel pretty exhausted and the straw is deep and warm up there.

I found a great feather behind the cow shed this morning. My dad told me it belonged to a "peasant" - at least that's what I think he called it. He got me carrying it around the yard in my mouth. He told me that it would give me a chance to get used to the feel. Really boring! I expect he'll start one of his lectures in a minute, about how superior Labradors are when it comes to retrieving. He usually goes off into a world of his own when he's spouting, so I'll take the opportunity to sneak off to the barn and give this feather a serious chewing."

Anticipation

In armchair reclining, with feet by the fire
My master relaxes and shows no desire
Or the least inclination to leave this warm place
Contentment is written all over his face.
The daylight is fading, the temperature low
The man on the wireless is forecasting snow,
So he smiles to himself and wriggles his toes
And tries not to let his bad conscience impose
On his comfort, but inwardly thinking that he
Should be out there defying the weather with me.

But I am a dog with my own special needs.
I like plenty of walking and regular feeds
So I sit by his side - gently paw at his leg,
To command his attention. I'm ready to beg
To bother and pester, 'til master complies
With the dogged requests from my soft pleading eyes.
But he shakes his head slowly and shoos me away
And says "It's too early, now go off and play
With a toy or a bone. It is my place to choose
When I put on my hat and my coat and my shoes."

I don't need a wristwatch to tell me the time
Or to hear the old clock on the mantelpiece chime.
I just stare at the front door with great expectation
My leash in my mouth and in anticipation
By yipping and whining and quietly crying
Make perfectly sure my behaviour is trying!
So that master, unable to get any peace
Will accept that from duty, there'll be no release.
- Then sighing, he rises, reluctant and slow
And says "I give in boy. I'm ready. Let's go."

Unspoken Words

It was early spring when I lost Mary. It had only been a month before Christmas that she'd been to see her doctor with the pain in her side and by then it was too late. It all occurred so fast. There was hardly any time to register what was happening and it was all over.

After the funeral, I shut down. I hardly ate or slept, I wouldn't answer the door, I just sat in the house listening to the silence. It wasn't a large house, but without Mary filling it with her chatter - her laughter - her soul - it felt like a huge dark cave, cold and empty. Even the echoes of her presence seemed to fade away to nothing.

I couldn't grieve. I knew that I needed to, but my whole body felt numb. It was like the sensation you experience when, rising from the dentists chair after a filling or extraction, you touch your face. Your fingers feel the cheek, but there's no reaction. It's as though your cheek belongs to someone else. That's how I felt, all over.

The only sensation of which I was aware, was the black hole. The empty gnawing void that had taken me over inside. I once read in a book on astronomy, that black holes are believed to suck in matter from the space around themselves. This one seemed to be sucking in my emotions - my very being - until I felt in danger of just collapsing in on myself and disappearing forever.

It was perhaps a week before I began to surface. Then Phillipa, my sister, came to see me. When she saw the state I was in, she told me that I should get away for a while. She suggested Scotland.

I'd had a passion for Scotland since I'd been a child. My parents had taken Phillipa and me to a small village on the west coast every summer, for about ten years. In that time I'd made friends with some of the local children. These friendships had grown with time, so that when my parents were unable to take us any more, I continued to go alone, staying with a friend and his widowed mother.

The village of Port Craige was just two rows of white-washed stone cottages, that cradled the shore of a small bay. The cuticle - like curve of the shore-line, was interrupted only by an old stone pier, that afforded some protection to an area of water from the heavy seas. At one time it had offered shelter to a small fishing fleet, but the days of the villagers' dependence on fish had long passed and these days most of the locals were employed on the land. There were still, however, a few small wooden boats bobbing below the pier, some of the men supplementing their agricultural wages by creeling for crab and lobster.

It only took one visit, prior to our marriage and as I'd anticipated, Mary was hooked. Having never been North of the border before, she fell instantly under the spell of the place. From then on we went together. Even our honeymoon was spent walking the mountains and cliffs around the port, visiting the coves and inlets that punctuated the high granite cliffs. These are places I'd known and explored when I'd been young, but I found unabashed delight in rediscovering them with my new wife.

For eight years we'd gone back together, sometimes twice a year. Now here I was returning alone.

As I rounded the last bend to the north of Port Craige, I pulled over and stopped the car on the grass verge. It was very dark and, killing the headlights, I stared across the bay to the twin rows of lights that blazed out from the warm and cosy dwellings. The tide was full and the lights reflected as long fragmented lines as they skipped and danced across the broken surface of the sea.

Mary used to say that this first sight of the port at night, reminded her of a ship in dock. You couldn't see the cottages, only their lights. S.S. Port Craige, she called it. As I sat there taking in that all too familiar scene, the black hole inside me seemed to grow a little, like the tumour that had grown in Mary. For me though, there seemed no release from the pain, from the hurt and the anguish that tossed and churned within, like the sea before me.

Morag McLean was Port Craige's postmistress. The post office was, by necessity, only small, but the house itself was the largest in the port. Most of the dwellings were low cottages, but the Posthouse, as it was known locally, stood out, being a two-storey building. It had once been the Village Inn, but had stopped trading as such just after the Second World War. Morag utilized the extra rooms by offering bed and breakfast accommodation. With no local competition she was kept constantly busy during the summer season and even out of season there seemed to be a steady trickle of custom. She always made sure, however, that she had room for us. Morag and I went back many years. Her son Robbie and I had been and still were, the very best of friends and it was she who had put me up (or should I say put up with me,) when I began coming to the port alone in my mid-teens.

Morag had been widowed twenty five years earlier, when Robbie was five. I have only vague memories of Gordon, her husband. He died tragically in a boat accident, not long after we started taking our holidays there. Although I was two years older than Robbie, we quickly developed a bond of friendship that had continued to the present day. He now worked and lived in Glasgow. He hadn't married, but every time we met up, he seemed to have a new girl in tow.

I'd spoken to him on the phone before I'd left, but due to pressures at work, he'd been unable to get away immediately, so I didn't expect to see him before the weekend.

Morag stood silhouetted in the Posthouse doorway. She didn't speak, she just stepped forward as I walked from the car and took me in her arms. We stood there silently embracing for several minutes. When we parted, I saw that there were tears filling her eyes and as I looked, one broke free of her lower lash and ran quickly down her pale cheek. It was she who broke the silence. "Hallo Toby, come in and get warm. It's a long drive."

Morag was like a second mother to me and I guess that having experienced sudden and unforeseen bereavement herself, she sensed what to say.

"Have you cried?" she asked, as we sat together by the open fire in the living room.

"I can't," I replied. "I've so much pain and anger trapped inside, Morag, but I can't seem to bring it out. It's here." I placed my outstretched hand on my own chest. "Just here, boiling and seething inside, but I don't know how to release it."

She looked into her lap where the fingers of her right hand slowly turned the gold band on her wedding finger. She didn't speak, just nodded slowly. It was a gesture of total understanding.

The following day I rose early, my appetite still subdued, so I only had a scant breakfast. I'd decided to go out and walk the hills behind the port, as Mary and I would have done. Morag filled a flask and cut some sandwiches and donning my old walking boots, I bade her goodbye and set out.

The day was dull and overcast. A fine drizzle was in the air, but the wind, which had been brisk the previous day, had calmed and despite the rain, it was surprisingly mild for the time of year.

I'd walked for several miles and was thinking of heading back when, topping a rise between the mountains and the sea, I looked down towards the coast. My attention was immediately drawn to a small flock of sheep, moving together in an unusual fashion. I was still some distance away, but looking closely, I noticed a smaller black and white shape darting to and fro, around and between the milling flock. Off to the right and lower down the hillside, I could make out the solitary figure of a man. He appeared motionless, but the shrill strains of a whistle drifted up to where I stood watching. Despite my regular visits to this remote part of the world, I had rarely seen a shepherd working his flock with a dog. It had always held a fascination for me, so I felt compelled to get nearer and watch the man and his dog, synchronized by patient training and silent understanding, working together as one. I moved down the slope until I came to an old dry-stone wall that traversed the hillside. By now I was close enough to watch easily and yet, if my presence was unwelcome, I felt that I would not be conspicuous behind the wall.

I don't know how long I stood there watching, but the afternoon was well under way when I suddenly realized how hungry I was. I hadn't felt so hungry since Mary had died and so devoured with some relish the packed lunch that Morag had put up for me.

I decided reluctantly to start heading back to The Port. The nights drew in quickly so early in the year so far North and I didn't want to worry Morag. As I made my way back, I couldn't help wondering why the shepherd had been there, working his sheep, without apparent motive. It was Morag who supplied the answer to my question.

"That'll be Drew Murdoch," she explained. "He and his dog Jester are entered in the county show. He goes up to Barnock Hill to put Jester through his paces. But that's part of his father's farm and you can often see them up there together anyway."

The following day I decided to go back to the Barnock and see if I could catch sight of Drew and Jester again. They had created a fascination in me, that I felt unable to deny.

I searched all morning and afternoon, both on and around the Barnock hill. A strange compulsion drove me on, irrationally, to catch sight once more of this total stranger and his dog.

It was early evening by the time I finally came across them. I'd given up hope and was, in fact, heading back. The sheep were feeding peacefully across the hillside and Drew and Jester were sitting quietly together. They must have just come up to enjoy the day's end, having been working elsewhere. Had they been out on the hills, I would surely have found them sooner.

The evening was indeed glorious. The air was breathless and long thin coils of blue-grey smoke snaked up from the pipe that jutted from the corner of Drew's mouth.

The previous night had been wild. The wind had risen and throughout the hours of darkness blustery squalls had raced in from the sea and battered the coast before moving inland. I'd tossed and turned in my bed, sleep eluding me; the storm creating a cacophony of wind and percussion, like incidental music to a waking nightmare.

By mid-morning the wind had died away again and brief glimpses of the sun occasionally pierced the ever-breaking cloud.

At the onset of evening the whole place was bathed in an almost ethereal calm and these were the conditions in which I finally came across Drew and Jester.

My eyes were suddenly drawn from the two figures below me to the vista that lay spread out beyond. It was breathtaking in its tranquil beauty. The slowly sinking sun had turned the sky to yellows, pinks and golds. To the North, the inshore islands of Seil, Luing and Shuna were dark against the reflected light on the water, as was the island of Scarba opposite. To the South-West, the Northern tip of Jura faded south to where The Paps, fainter with distance, thrust upwards like the breasts of a reclining female form. Peppered liberally across the intervening waters between these larger islands, numerous smaller rocks and islets lay scattered haphazardly, like the drips of paint on a Jackson Pollock canvas. Some were so small that they only peeped shyly above the waves at low tide, while others were large enough to support their own mantle of green baize. Beyond the inner islands to the North-West lay the mountains of Mull, showing pale blue and purple in the evening light.

I'd intended to speak to Drew if I found him again, to express my pleasure and fascination at watching him and his dog work together the day before. Standing there on the hillside however and looking down on the scene below I felt that to interrupt would have been an intrusion.

As I watched the unspoken communion between them, Drew turned to look at his companion. He lifted his hand to stroke and caress Jester's head and as he did so, Jester raised his paw and gently laid it in Drew's lap. From somewhere inside I felt the first stirrings of emotion, as if a tiny rupture had appeared in the black hole and allowed some faint trace of feeling to escape.

I wanted to stay and watch them all night, but eventually Drew stood up. Jester rose to follow his master, away across the fields. Drew slowly vanished into the gloom with Jester close to heel.

It was dark by the time I reached the Posthouse. The last half-mile proved quite hazardous, stumbling across rough fields my only illumination being starlight and the residual glow that still faintly stained the horizon. The lights of Port Craige were like beacons to me. Even from behind and above, they drew me safely to my destination.

As I entered the house, I could plainly see the relief on Morag's face, but she made no comment. She just squeezed my arm gently, smiled and disappeared into the kitchen to make tea.

Later that night, as we sat by the fire once more, I talked about my experiences on the mountain. How I'd actually felt some emotion seeping through and how, for the first time in weeks, my awareness of the pain inside had actually diminished, as my fascination with that lonely figure and his dog had grown. Morag placed her hand on mine and again there was a gentle squeeze. "Good," she said earnestly. "Perhaps the healing has begun."

For the next two days, the weather closed in again, preventing me from going far. A cold front, moving in from the Atlantic, brought high winds and driving rain. This gradually subsided to squally showers and even the occasional snow flurry. Between the showers, I ventured out and wondered along the beach.

The heavy weather had torn seaweed from its bedrock anchors and the sand was almost obscured in places by great rafts of dark green fronds and tendrils. The howling gusts, which almost lifted me from my feet at times, rolled and tossed gobbets of foam from wave-crest and water-line, across sand and weed, to be deposited in frothy drifts at the base of the dune line. Even the boats that lay in the relative shelter of the old pier, danced at their moorings like marionettes.

Through it all, the constant cry of gulls pierced the tumult of rushing wind and waves. They sailed with consummate ease on the buffeting air, or bobbed comically on the surface of the water, riding the roller-coaster of peak and trough.

At the far end of the beach, where sand and rocks met, a small huddle of Oystercatchers, the pied-pipers of the shore, cooed and trilled to each other. Out of sight, amongst the dunes, a lone Curlew delivered its mournful call, that rose in pitch and tempo. Mary had always found their cries so sad. She'd been filled with awe and wonder at the sheer number and variety of birds that seemed to be constantly present around The Port. She'd taken great delight in learning their names and many varied calls.

My thoughts were interrupted by the Curlew crying out once more and as I looked towards the dunes, I saw the bird itself, rise from amongst the grassy tussocks that capped the low mounds of sand. As it departed, its long sickle-shaped beak and trailing legs were silhouetted clearly against the lighter sky, while its fading call seemed to taunt me and say, "I can grieve for her, why not you?"

By the Friday morning the worst of the storm had passed. The rain had gone and the steely grey skies of the previous two days were again broken by flecks of blue. The wind was still brisk though and the clouds scudded overhead at a break-neck speed.

Robbie was due to arrive that evening, but in the meantime, I decided to return to Barnock Hill.

Having been unable to get out for two days. I found myself excited at the prospect of searching out Drew and Jester once more. This strange fascination seemed to border on obsession and I couldn't explain it. It was as though they held the key to a riddle that, along with my grief, was locked up inside me. As such I felt drawn inexorably to them.

A short time later I topped the ridge of Barnock once more. I looked down to where I'd seen my quarry on the previous occasions. I immediately felt that something was wrong. About halfway down the slope, a black-faced ewe was bawling continually. At her feet I could distinguish a small white mass. From that distance it was unrecognizable, but her cries appeared strained and full of anguish. I was suddenly aware of a swiftly moving black and white form closing in on the ewe from lower down the hillside - Jester. Bringing up the rear came the hurrying figure of Drew himself.

They closed in on the spot where the ewe continued to cry, her pitiful calls rising and falling as they rolled around the surrounding hills.

Jester's close proximity appeared to unsettle the ewe, but she seemed unwilling to relinquish the ground she held. He lay down several yards from her, presumably on some command from Drew, which I neither saw nor heard. There he waited for his master to arrive. On reaching the spot, Drew fell to his knees beside the small shape that lay half hidden in the grass. The ewe moved away to a safe distance but continued to call plaintively. I saw Drew reach down and raise the motionless form. It was only then that I was able to see what it was.

The limp and lifeless body of a new-born lamb drooped like a rag doll across his lap. As I stood there that Friday morning in April, the wind puffed and panted around me, causing my eyes to sting and water. Below me the tragic little scene seemed to reach its climax. Drew, kneeling in the damp grass – his head bowed in unmistakable sorrow, gently stroked the inert form that lay across his legs. As he did so Jester rose and padded to his master's side. He sat down so close that he appeared to be actually leaning against Drew's right arm and began gently licking the man's inclined face. I wondered whether there were tears on his cheeks and, if so, were they due to the wind or to sorrow?

It was then I felt the first stirrings down in the black hole. There was nothing sudden about it. It was a gradual process. The sensation built as an eruption might, growing in intensity deep underground. Then, like lava rising through volcanic vents, I felt a welling up inside. The pressure in me grew and grew to a point where I could bear it no longer. Suddenly, it exploded; a colossal scream that echoed round and round the surrounding hills. It kept coming and coming – pouring out; the unstoppable flow of molten rock from the crater.

Encapsulated in that great paroxysm was the whole of my grief, my pain and anger, that had lain caged and festering inside me for three weeks. As my lungs emptied and the scream faded, I fell to my knees and drew in a long gasping breath. I felt like someone who had been plunged into deep water and, struggling back to the surface again, sucks in the first lung-full of clear, fresh, wonderful air.

Then the tears came, Not the false tears of the wind, but the real tears of deep sorrow. I wept for the lamb and its wailing mother, for the shepherd and his loss. I wept for Morag and Robbie's grief at Gordon's tragic passing and I cried for my own self-pity and loneliness. But most of all I wept for Mary, whose sweet voice and merry laughter would no longer fill my life and whose personal hopes and aspirations would never now be fulfilled. She was at least at peace though, after the cruel and cutting pain she'd endured.

I don't know how long I knelt there weeping, but when I at last looked up, the shepherd and his dog were no longer visible. The mother's cries had died away to the occasional call of all sheep and there I was, alone on a Scottish hillside. As I rose to make my way back to The Port, I felt, as Morag had suggested, that the healing had indeed begun. Although I still felt the pain and loss of Mary's passing, it was tempered by another emotion, still faint, but undeniable. Hope had once more returned to me and I now felt that I could at least begin to rebuild my life.

Guiding Lights

We are the chosen, the privileged few
With a calling in life, to be faithful and true
To the task we were bred for; our reason for living
To be constant and steadfast and selfless in giving
With total devotion our love and protection,
By earning their trust and by giving direction.
Unswerving companion and comrade in need
Our training prepares us for our special deed
To steer them through danger unerring and sure
By being their eyes, - to keep them secure!

At six weeks of age with excitement and pride
And with tense expectation we sit side by side.
The start of our schooling, for twelve months duration
Is to go out to "walkers" for socialization
And while in their care we will start to adjust
To the world that we live in and also to trust
In the people that care, and so feel much remorse
When we leave to embark on the forty-week course.
Then, if we are worthy, a month from the end
We will finally meet our new partner and friend.

So we ponder and guess what the future might hold
And hope beyond hope - when we reach two years old
That we all make the grade - to be fine
    working creatures
And by doing our best for our trainers and teachers
We'll hold our heads high, whilst we pity the few
That just didn't make it and failed to get through.
With our master or mistress we'll form a close bond
Be ready to face every challenge beyond,
Though sadly unable to give back their sight
We'll shine through their darkness - their true
    guiding light!

Wet and Dry

As someone who was not brought up with dogs, nothing could have prepared me for the revelations I'd experience on making their acquaintance for the first time. In my youth, I'd obviously been aware of dogs but they were other people's pets. I neither liked nor disliked them. To me, a dog was just a dog!

It wasn't until my early twenties, when I became friends with the Cartwrights, that my lack of canine companionship was rectified. Thomas and Joyce Cartwright were friends of a friend from college. We met at a dinner party and immediately it was as if we were old friends. They were much older than me and as both my mother and father were dead, they became a bit like second parents. In the arrogance of youth, I never really considered what they found so interesting about me. They were themselves childless, although I never felt that I was some kind of surrogate son. I was always treated as an equal.

Tommy was an architect by profession, so I don't suppose money was ever a real problem. They owned a converted crofter's cottage at the head of a small glen in the Southern Uplands of Scotland. The cottage was called Dunkeln. It was only a holiday retreat, but they adored it. They thought nothing of making the near three hundred mile journey on a Friday night, just to spend the weekend there, returning in the early hours of Monday morning. Indeed as Tommy's business carried him off round the world periodically and as Joyce had an innate dread of flying, they spent much of their free time and holidays at Dunkeln.

As I've mentioned, the Cartrights were childless. They did, however, own two dogs, a pair of wonderful English Springer Spaniels. They were my first introduction to dogs, and what an introduction!

Buster was a large black and white 'dog' Springer. As his name implied, he had the temperament of a tank. Once he'd made his mind to do something, nothing and no one got in his way. The deepest thicket and the densest undergrowth were no barrier to Buster, but his greatest joy was water! The smallest puddle or the widest river were like magnets to him. He just loved being near it, on it, but most of all, in it. Joyce would hold up her hands in despair as once again he returned from his walk soaking wet and covered in mud. "I reckon he's got a divining rod stuck up his nose!", she'd say, smiling wryly "Even if we lived in a desert and there was no water to be found, Buster would come home wet!" Despite her moans she adored him and he, in turn, was devoted to her. Although Tommy had some control over him, Joyce was the only person to whom Buster would truly respond.

Meg, on the other hand, was the complete opposite to Buster. A liver and white Springer bitch, she was smaller and much less robust than the big guy. She was quieter and almost dainty in her ways.

As Buster was to Joyce, so Meg was to Tommy, completely loyal and totally devoted. She never wandered more than a few yards from his side when out walking, so while Buster was off scouring the hills and valleys for smells (and of course water) Meg would always be in sight, no more than a stone's throw away. Oh yes, she hated water!

As my friendship with the Cartrights grew, I was invited to stay at Dunkeln for a few days periodically. In time I would spend as much as three weeks with them. You'd think that being in such close proximity (the cottage had only two bedrooms, a small bathroom and a kitchen/dining room) we would have got on each other's nerves. But no, we just seemed to fit together, like pieces of a jig-saw puzzle. Those were probably the best years of my bachelor life, they were also the fittest, as most of our days were spent walking the hills and mountains around the glen where Dunkeln stood. It was a glorious and awe-inspiring place - not as grand and dramatic as the Highlands to the North, but breathtaking in its subdued magnificence. Sometimes just two of us would go out, more often all three, but always the dogs would be there, Meg close by and Buster roaming far and wide.

In the evenings, we'd sit by an open fire, the glowing coals and flickering flames casting that wonderful warm and all-enveloping aura around us. We'd talk about everything and nothing late into the night, while the dogs snoozed blissfully, Meg at Tommy's feet and Buster at Joyce's. Every now and then, one of them would give a little whimper and there'd be a slight twitch of tail or paw as they dreamed doggy dreams. There was a TV set, but the reception was poor and anyway, no one seemed interested in what was happening beyond the glen.

High above the cottage and about a mile and a half distant, there was a small Loch which nestled in a depression on the mountain side. I could never pronounce its Gaelic name, but the locals referred to it as "Rabbie's Tarn". We were only a few miles from Glen Trool, the site of Robert the Bruce's first successful battle against the English - presumably after his legendary encounter with the spider in the cave.

Local folk-lore had it that Rabbie Bruce (as they call him) stopped at the tarn to rest and contemplate his battle plans before moving out to meet his enemies in Glen Trool. I've no idea whether there's any truth in the story, but I guess it's as good a tale as any, and I could at least pronounce "Rabbie's Tarn".

The Loch, however, did play its part in my time at Dunkeln. You see, whichever route we'd take on our many excursions, they all seemed to end up beside the Loch.

We'd always stop by its still waters to rest and maybe take some refreshment. It was a magical place, whose atmosphere reminded me of a church or cathedral. I'm not a religious man but I always felt closer to something higher in that place. If Rabbie Bruce had indeed visited that Loch prior to his encounter with the English, I'm sure he would have left there with his spirit charged by the experience. I use the expression "still water" because however windy the day was, the natural contours of the surrounding hills seemed to shelter this particular spot. My memories of Rabbie's Tarn are only of glass like tranquillity and ethereal calm - that is of course until Buster arrived on the scene! Straight in he'd go, barking wildly and ploughing through the shallows at the edge, before swimming out into deeper water. The bow waves produced by his chin as he cut through the mirror - like surface, would fan out slowly, finally reaching the shore, where the tiny wavelets would break on the pebbled fringes. Throughout all of this Meg would sit quietly at the water's edge, watching the big guy make a complete fool of himself. When we eventually had to leave the Loch side to continue our walk, Buster would reluctantly emerge from his aquatic revelry and, as a display of apparent protest at being compelled to leave his natural element, he'd come right up to us before shaking the excess water from his coat! As the peace had initially been shattered by Buster's arrival at the Loch, our departure was usually marked by our yells of complaint as we were liberally showered by a very disgruntled dog!

All that was many years ago. I'm married now with two children. I also have two dogs of my own. They are, of course, Springer Spaniels. Litter sisters, as different as chalk and cheese. We're still great friends with the Cartrights although they're both getting on in years. Tommy suffers quite badly from arthritis, so he's unable to drive very far these days. Joyce never learned to drive and eventually they had to sell Dunkeln. It was a terrible wrench for them both. They offered it to me at an extremely reasonable price, but I was only recently married at the time and trying to cope with a mortgage, bills and all the other pressures of being newly wed. I was, sadly, not in a position to accept.

Buster lived to be fifteen. At about twelve years old he had a run-in with two German Shepherds. Any sensible Springer would have made a tactical retreat, but not Buster! He lost an eye in the encounter, but had the satisfaction of chasing both dogs away. Even with the loss of an eye, he never changed until the day he died - stubborn and self-willed to the end!

Meg developed a lump on her side when she was eight years old. It turned out to be malignant and she had to be put to sleep. Her passing was mourned by all who knew that delightful, gentle and sensitive creature, but most especially by Tommy who missed her dreadfully.

As someone who was not brought up with dogs, I can only imagine that had it not been for my friendship with the Cartrights and my subsequent involvement with their two wonderful and enchanting dogs, my life would probably have been less colourful and maybe - just maybe - I'd have been a lesser person for that.

Squatters Rights

There once was a time in long bye-gone days
When I ruled like a queen over all she surveys
The kitchen, the garden, the bedrooms and hall
The bathroom, the staircase, the parlour and all.
And those who existed within that domain
Were mine to command - to over them reign.
The humans that fed me and pampered each whim
Named Alice and Albert and Betty and Jim
Were there just to serve me and give me their all
To fuss and to spoil me; at my beck and call.

As well as the people who lived with me there
Were two old retainers - permitted to share
The house and the garden that I called my home
A Springer named Jess and a Lab called Gerome.
When they had been puppies, they'd both been a pain
Uncouth and stubborn - and difficult to train
But as they got older and slow in their ways
With grey fur and stiff limbs, (they'd seen better days)
They found that to argue and fight with me still
Was a waste of their time so they bent to my will.

Ah, those were the days, I dream of them yet
When the only bad thing was a trip to the vet.
If I wanted some fuss or felt like a nap
I'd go to a human - curl up on their lap.
If I wanted adventure I'd wander outside
To stalk little birdies and catch them - I tried
To creep up behind them and take them off guard
(I've caught one or two in my jungle back yard)
Then back to the parlour all cosy and snug
To sit by the fire, to groom on the rug.

Then everything changed, it's a year to the day
That old Jessie expired and her soul slipped away
And lonely without her, he couldn't get through
The long empty days so, Gerome passed on too.
With fond recollection, I look back with pride
That they both knew their place and would move to one side
When I entered a room, or passed in the hall.
They showed me respect, even though I was small
How I long for those days when my life was so good
And I governed supreme, just as a cat should!

You'd think that the honour to have only me
Would be more than enough, but it wasn't to be
For the humans decided a dog must be bought
A replacement they said and obviously thought
That I wouldn't mind. "She'll accept it' they said
And they didn't consult, simply took it as read
That of course I'd comply with whatever they chose
And not make a fuss or turn up my nose.
But I am a feline both regal and royal
To treat me so badly, it makes my blood boil!

Then came the day that they brought the dog home
A little Jack Russell who wanted to roam
All over my house and my garden as well
With one aim in mind, to deposit his smell
On every conceivable item and wall.
He stank out the kitchen, the parlour and hall.
But worse than his odour - no notice you see
Did he take of his betters - especially me!
All objects that moved were to him just a game
And pity me do, I was treated the same!

Coming into the house - he would chase me around.
If I sat out of reach, he would bark 'til the sound
Of his yapping and whining would drive me insane
And even the humans would have to restrain
Him and fasten him up in the garage or shed
While I gained composure beneath Betty's bed.
He was vulgar and coarse and especially rude
When he'd scare me at meal times - then eat up my food!
But the worst thing he'd do and which made me see red
Was to climb in my basket and sleep on my bed!

Now my world is uncertain and riddled with fears
As I watch my old empire collapse round my ears.
Although they still feed me and show me affection
I am rarely relaxed, don't know the direction
From which the tormenter from hell will appear.
What a thrill would I get, could I rip off his ear
Or scratch out his eyes - claw him slowly to death.
How smugly I'd purr as he took his last breath.
But my claws aren't as sharp now - I'm well past my prime
I'm a monarch in exile just biding my time.

Nigel Hemming

In The Dog House

"Ah, yes! Is that Mr Williams?

Oh good! It's Phil Gordon here - from the farm.

Yes, that's right! Hello!

I'm sorry to bother you, but, as you've probably guessed, it's about my dogs.

I've just got in and my wife's told me about them getting out, so I thought I'd better ring and apologise. Have they done much damage?

Oh really! Did they? I see! The chickens you say. Have you lost any? Well! Thank goodness for that at least.

Have they done any other damage? The wire. Can it be easily repaired? Oh good! You will of course send me the bill.

Well Mr Williams, I'm really very sorry. Let me reassure you that we've found where they got out and I shall be ensuring that they won't escape that way again. I shall also be making sure that there aren't any other places that they might get through.

Well, that's very understanding Mr Williams, I do appreciate your patience.

It's Millie you see. Yes, she's the black Lab. Yes, I'm sure she was the real culprit. Really? Well, I'm not at all surprised!

She's only just twelve months old and ever since we've had her she's been nothing but trouble.

Oh yes! She is very sweet and we love her to bits, but she's a real monkey.

It's Tara that I'm really surprised at. That's right, our old springer. She's usually so sensible.

I know! We've never had any trouble with her. Well! Not until we had Millie anyway. We hoped that she'd teach Millie some of the basics, but judging from today's little escapade, it would appear to be the other was round - More's the pity!

So, when did you realize they were in your garden?

Oh! The chickens gave it away then.

It's a good job you were in.

Yes, it could have been disastrous if you hadn't been home.

Was it both of them that got into the coop?

Just Millie eh?

So where was Tara then?

What! Just sitting by the gate?

So she didn't actually come into the garden? But she didn't bark, or give the game away?

The little devil.

Well, once again Mr Williams, thank you for being so understanding. As I've said, I'll make quite sure they don't get out again, and let me assure you, they know they're in trouble. I can see them from here, through the kitchen window. They're looking very sorry for themselves.

Yes. And to you Mr Williams, and give my best wishes to your wife.

I will indeed.

Right! Goodbye, yes, goodbye."

Found

The old shepherd's gaze wandered up through the valley,

His flock was at risk, there was no time to dally,

The late snow had taken him quite by surprise,

The barometer glass had started to rise

When he'd tapped it in passing the evening before.

As he wended his way to his bed he felt sure

That the winter had finally made way for spring.

With the onset of lambing - warm weather would bring

New grass that the ewes on his pastures would need

For production of milk so their off-spring could feed.

When he'd woken that morning and opened his eyes,

It should have been dark as he started to rise,

But his senses, though clouded, detected a change,

The luminous glow from his window was strange

And the sounds of the morning were muted and dull -

The call of the sheep and the cry of a gull.

Then pulling the old cotton curtains aside

He shook his head slowly and desperately tried

To grasp that his world had transformed over night

From soft browns and greens into brilliant white.

Having gathered his wits and got over the shock,

His initial concern was the state of his flock.

Some ewes had lambs and with others "expecting"

By not taking action he would be neglecting

His duty - so not to brook further delay

He gathered his clothes from the previous day

And throwing them on, (there was no time to waste)

He stumbled downstairs with unusual haste

Then across to the peg for his hat and his coat

Took hold of a scarf - wrapped it tight round his throat.

From the shadowy depths of the scullery door
Came the scratching of claws on the quarry-tiled floor
Their tails were held high they were wagged to and fro
And happy to see him they cried soft and low
He reached out his hands and placed each on a head
And with warmth in his voice he quietly said
"Hallo my beauties, there's trouble outside"
Then drawing the bolts, he pulled the door wide.
He took a step back to let the dogs through
Saying, "Come on my lovelies there's hard work to do."

The morning drew on as he searched for his sheep
(In places the snow drifts were several feet deep)
But he knew that he'd have to account for them all
Especially the lambs - which because they were small
Were unable to cope with such terrible cold
So this drove him on, even though he was old
And arthritic pain when conditions were bad
Would make his joints ache - but he knew that he had
To keep up the search - cover all of the ground
And not take a rest 'til the last one was found.

Now high on the hill, by the reservoir dam
There was still one ewe missing along with her lamb.
He knew her as Floss - she was one of the best -
She was older and wiser than all of the rest.
If not rescued soon they would never survive
His hope faded fast that he'd find them alive
Then from deep in a drift, grown especially big
Came the faintest of sounds, so he started to dig.
Safe and well in a pocket of air she had been
Old Floss, but no trace of her lamb could be seen.

Then he cried out aloud with his arms in the air
The loss of just one filled his heart with despair
And the pitiful calls of the ewe at his side
Only deepened his grief even though he had tried
With an effort supreme for a man of his years.
Now, his energy spent, his old eyes filled with tears
But suddenly sadness reverted to hope
As born on the breeze and from high up the slope
Came the weakest of calls. The old man gave a shout
To his dogs, "Go my beauties and search the lamb out."

Up sprang the dogs with a leap and a bound
They both knew their duty - the lost must be found!
Though weary themselves, they had no reservation
About his command and without hesitation
Each quartered the hill with his nose to the ground
Ears pricked and alert for the feeblest sound.
On cresting the brow of a difficult rise
Below, on a ledge, lay their ultimate prize.
The dogs barked in triumph to let master know
As he waited with Floss in the valley below.

Toiling through snow that lay deep on the hill
The call of the dogs renewed the man's will
Though cold and exhausted - with hope driven on
That finally, here was the last little one
But what was its fate? Was it safe? Was it lost?
Could it live through the chill of the snow and the frost?
On reaching the place where his precious dogs sat
He smiled and spoke softly, gave each one a pat
And his heart leapt for joy, for he now knew for sure
That the last of his flock was found - safe and secure!

Beneath his old coat and tucked under his arm
The shepherd ensured the lamb came to no harm
As he carried it back to its mother below.
But exhaustion and snow meant that progress was slow
And as he came down the sun suddenly broke
Through the lowering cloud and started to soak
The hills and the valleys in crisp winter light
To the shepherd's old eyes this incredible sight
Made him stop in his tracks and quietly say
"Praise the Lord for success - and this glorious day."

Golden Sands

If you've ever watched a butterfly or moth emerging from a chrysalis, you'll have some idea of the sight that greeted me that first morning. David Briggs is my oldest and dearest friend. We go back nearly twenty years to when we were at school together. I think it's fair to say that there's only one person to whom I'm closer and that's my wife Ann.

David lay on the bed at the far end of the caravan, cocooned in his sleeping bag. It was the type with a hood and separate arms that, David assured me, "were used by mountaineers. Bags like this have been up Everest" he'd pointed out. "You can't get better than this." I think he'd borrowed it from his brother-in-law, who'd been a bit of an outdoors sort of chap when he was younger. It must have been well insulated as there were beads of sweat blooming all over David's face, at least what I could see of it. Only his bright red nose and his eyes were visible through the draw-strung porthole in the sleeping bag's hood.

My own bed was one of the long bench seats that made up part of the dining area at the front of the van. When Ann and I came away with the children, the whole of this forward area could be converted into a huge bed, while the kids - James our son, who's ten and Elizabeth who's eight - slept in the rear section where David now lay.

It hadn't been easy, persuading Ann to let me come away with David, especially in our caravan. She didn't dislike David, in fact, she had rather a soft spot for him. She'd actually known David longer than I had, being a friend of his sister, but I know she found some of his habits and attitudes rather trying at times. You see, David was a bit of a know-all. He was also rather lazy. It was probably these characteristics that, at least in part, accounted for the reason that I found myself lying there that morning.

David's marriage was on the rocks.

When David and Kim decided to take the plunge, everyone who knew them thought that the whole thing was doomed. Nobody really considers a couple's suitability while they're simply going out together. Boyfriend - girlfriend relationships are fluid and casual and are accepted on that level - no matter how long they last. However, the minute a ring is given, plans laid and preparations made, everybody suddenly becomes an armchair shrink or agony aunt. They tear the relationship to shreds, trying to analyse and evaluate the couple's chances of succeeding in marriage. Of course, this is all done behind the couple's back. To their faces, everything is sweetness and light. Lots of drinks bought to celebrate, face-splitting grins, laughter and much slapping of backs.

Indeed, I think that of all David and Kim's friends, Ann and I were the only two that thought that, at least from David's point of view, Kim was the best thing that had ever happened.

Ann is right, David is a know-all. Not in a really annoying way, like some people. There's nothing worse than someone who tries to tell you that black is white, when you know it's red. David isn't like that; he's a highly intelligent chap. He's got grade one O and A levels coming out of his ears, not to mention a first class honours degree in Classics. You see, he really is very knowledgeable. I know he doesn't mean to be, but people find him a bit irritating at times, particularly when he starts telling them all about something deep that's fascinating to him and which he understands in the greatest detail, but to the less enlightened holds absolutely no interest whatsoever.

Our friendship has probably lasted over the years because I accept him for what he is. I don't judge or criticize him too harshly. In fact, I actually find him quite fascinating - even when he's off on one of his rambles about a subject I know absolutely nothing about I'm still glued to his every word. It's his enthusiasm I find so compelling. If you add to this the fact that I'm one of the few people who can actually get away with telling him to shut up when he does go too far, then perhaps you'll understand why we get on so well.

Kim first appeared on the scene about two years after Ann and I got married. They'd met through work and to my knowledge it was the first proper relationship that David had ever had.

David wasn't in fact, bad looking, but he'd never really shown an interest in the opposite sex and was, therefore, not unduly bothered about his appearance. There was never any suggestion that he was gay - God help him if there had been in an all-boys' school - but he was just preoccupied with more cerebral matters. So, while the rest of us lads struggled through puberty - waging war on acne - trying to style our hair in the latest fashions, (while at the same time, finding copious quantities of the stuff springing up in every conceivable nook and crany of our bodies!) While our soprano voices descended to tenors and below and our hitherto petite forms stretched into great lanky bean-poles, David seemed unaffected by any of it and, apparently, sailed through it all paying little heed.

In many ways, when I look back on that period of our lives, I'm rather envious of him. Being a typical Piscean by nature - artistic and with a tendency to be somewhat emotional - adolescence was a bit of a nightmare for me. My hormones began to simmer, and finally boil, quite early - my face exploding into a relief map of the Alps and, as I appeared to be a rather inadequate specimen of pubescent masculinity, I watched in despair and frustration as other members of my peer group started going out with girls. While my friends seemed interested in only one thing - at that age it was merely a quick fumbling grope - I had an additional handicap to contend with. While I also suffered the uncontrollable stirings and bulges in my trousers - usually at the most inopportune and embarrassing moments - I also had the annoying habit of falling head over heels in love with every pretty girl with whom I came into contact. As I didn't seem to have what it took to attract girls at the time, I was, therefore, constantly racked with unrequited love. Even when I was a few years older and I did finally manage to charm or con the occasional girl into a relationship, it never lasted long. This was usually because I was so besotted with them that the intensity of my feelings and manic, possessive behaviour, usually ended up driving them away.

Despite all of this emotional turmoil and anguish going on around him, David simply cruised along. He kept his head in his books and just smiled with only passing interest, as one of the lads related, (no doubt in highly exaggerated detail,) his latest exploit with some girl or other.

Although being something of an outsider, David was, nevertheless, quite popular amongst his class mates. He was never going to be one of the lads, but he did manage to avoid the torture and cruelty that school boys are prone to dispense, especially to kids that don't conform to their somewhat narrow views of what manhood is about. I never could understand how we escaped this nightmare. I'd seen what bullies were capable of - in fact I'd fallen foul of one myself. Ironically, on that particular occasion, it was David who'd saved my bacon.

I can't remember what I'd actually done to fall victim of this unpleasant individual. He was a couple of years above me and for some reason he wanted my blood. Before I suffered the beating I felt was inevitable, David appeared from nowhere and quietly spoke to him. I found out later that he'd offered to do his homework for him, should he let me off. David's reputation as a brainbox went before him in the school and, after a few seconds that felt like an eternity to me, his neanderthal brain had managed to grasp and process the offer being made. To my relief the great oaf loped off, knuckles dragging on the ground - no doubt to swing from the trees, eat bananas and pick parasites from his puss-ridden body.

Although we'd got on well with each other up to that point, I think that that episode marked the real beginning of our deeper and lasting friendship. You see, I believe it illustrated the primary reason that David was treated with respect by his fellow pupils. He's kind and considerate. He's a nice guy. People who know him simply can't help liking him, in spite of his little foibles.

When Ann and I met and married David was my best man. He'd just left university with a First Class Honours Degree and the world was his oyster. He actually turned up on the day with a young girl on his arm - something that caused us some consternation and embarrassment - as neither of us knew anything about her. David, we found out later was himself rather embarrassed at being the best man and not having a partner. He'd got it into his head that the best man should be "accompanied" at a wedding so, without saying a word to us, he asked a friend from University if she'd mind being his escort for the day. When he turned up on the morning of the ceremony at my flat with this girl in tow it rather put the cat amongst the pigeons. The church was obviously no problem, but the reception was! We'd only booked and paid for a fixed number of guests. In desperation, I phoned Ann and explained what had happened. Ann, who isn't at her best under pressure, went ballistic at me over the phone. I was accused of having friends whose sole purpose in life was to undermine her happiness and to ruin the most important day of her life. I finally managed to calm her down and said that I'd sort it out, realizing, just too late, that there was absolutely no reason to have phoned her in the first place. I then telephoned the hotel that was laying on the reception and quickly filled them in on the situation. They agreed to set one more place, at no extra cost. God bless them!!

I must confess that sitting in the church that day I really wasn't sure whether or not Ann would turn up. O course she did, in time honoured style and about five minutes late. The rest of the day went off like clockwork.

David's speech was, as I'd expected, a real gem. He could, when prepared, totally enthral and mesmerize an audience with his shy charm and razor-sharp wit. The girl with whom he'd come was rather plain to look at and she was equally lacking in charisma. I can't even remember her name now, but no matter - Ann and I never set eyes on her again.

David's ability to catch us unawares, at least where women were concerned, took us by surprise again exactly twelve months later. We'd had our own private first anniversary celebration on the appropriate day, but we decided that it would be nice to have a small dinner party for our close friends who had been involved in our wedding. Bridesmaids, ushers and best man. To our disappointment, nearly everyone who was invited was unable to come - all except David! Nevertheless, we decided to have the meal anyway. On the Saturday morning that David was due to come round, I decided to phone him, just to confirm that he was still coming. Past experience had taught me to leave nothing to chance where David was considered. We spoke for several minutes, chatting generally. I was just about to put down the receiver when David suddenly announced that he'd got a girl-friend and - would it be alright if he brought her along? The statement was made with such nonchalance that you'd have thought he was announcing the purchase of a new pet goldfish.

Ann's initial reaction to the news was irritation. David, true to form, cocking-up arrangements again. However, as time went on and the hour of the couple's arrival approached, curiosity began to take over and by the time the door bell rang at eight o'clock, we were both totally consumed by it.

Human nature being what it is, Ann and I tried to imagine what this, (as yet unknown female) might be like. We had however absolutely no criterion on which to base our musings. David had not hitherto had any girlfriends so we had no idea what type of girl he might be attracted to. As the only other girl that we'd actually seen him with was the infinitely forgettable individual he'd brought to our wedding, I must confess that our mental pictures tended to be rather negative.

True to form, Kim was absolutely nothing like the girl we had imagined. She was actually rather attractive in a subdued sort of way. She was very bright and effervescent, with a keen sense of humour. She was also nobody's fool. It turned out that this was only their second proper date, but it was soon quite obvious that she had David's measure. As I've already said, David could sometimes be a bit of a know-all. He was also prone to be a little pompous, particularly in mixed company. On more than one occasion that evening, when David was beginning to get a little carried away, Kim put him in his place. Not in a sharp or acidic way, but with gentle humorous comments that diffused the moment softly and with warmth. By the end of the evening, both Ann and I were totally enamoured by her.

As David had been my best man, so I was his when he and Kim were married about a year later. By that time, Kim was almost as close a friend as David - especially to Ann. I was absolutely thrilled that my old mate had finally found someone to settle down with and, as I believed, just the right girl too.

In those early years we often went around together. We even went away on holiday on a couple of occasions. Both David and Kim were God-parents to our children but after that we started to drift apart. We didn't fall out - indeed we were still the very best of friends. On the odd occasions that we did get together we had a wonderful time. Inevitably though, when the children came along, our time was rather limited and what free time we had we were usually too exhausted to use.

It was due to our increasing lack of contact that neither Ann nor I had the slightest hint of the crisis that was apparently brewing in the Briggs' household.

Two years ago David and Kim had moved away. David's job had taken him down South. With one hundred and fifty miles now separating us the only contact we had was the occasional letter and the exchange of cards on birthdays and at Christmas.

It was therefore quite a shock when, just a week after we'd sent them a wedding anniversary card, David suddenly turned up on our doorstep - unannounced as usual.

He was obviously very low and promptly informed us that he'd decided that he and Kim were having a trial separation. I asked him how Kim felt about this and he simply said that it was for the best. Ann, as you can imagine, was not too pleased at having David descend on us like that, although she did agree to put him up for a few nights. I don't think he actually had anywhere else to go as both his parents were dead and his sister was living abroad.

Ann secretly telephoned Kim to let her know that David was with us. She also hoped to find out what was going on. Kim was upset and worried and so relieved to hear that David was safe. She either couldn't or wouldn't be specific over the phone, but it had something to do with starting a family.

Being self-employed, I was able, within reason, to take time off at will and it was at this point that I suggested to David that he and I went away for a few days in the caravan.

That's how I found myself waking up that morning, staring at the mummy-like form of David, cocooned in his sleeping bag.

Now as well as two children, Ann and I also shared our home with a pair of the most splendid golden retrievers. A beautiful bitch called Lear and a magnificent dog called Macbeth, but not surprisingly, we tended to call him Mac. As you'll have guessed from the names, they were a reflection of Ann's passion for Shakespeare. Originally, we were going to call them Macbeth and Lady, but I said that I preferred Lear.

Having persuaded Ann to let us come away, she was adamant that we took the dogs with us. Although officially Mac was mine and Lear Ann's, it was I who did most of the "necessary", where the two animals were concerned. Ann loved them both with a passion - indeed it was she who pushed to have them in the first place. She had been raised with dogs, whereas I had not. I'd only been initiated into the canine world when I met Ann. She'd had an old collie when we'd married - Micky, a super old chap. He was twelve when we met and was well past his prime. Ann practically worshipped the ground which he walked on, but realized that he wasn't going to last forever. Within a couple of years of our marriage, when Mick was nearly fifteen, our local vet suggested that it might be an idea if we thought about getting a new dog before we lost him.

That's how Mac and Lear arrived on the scene. We'd only intended to have one, but when we saw them, at five weeks old, looking totally irresistible, curled up with their brothers and sisters, it didn't take very much persuading on Ann's part to get me to agree to have both remaining pups.

As Ann was kept very busy with the house and the kids, the canine duties naturally fell on me. It would have been unreasonable to expect Ann to stay at home and look after the dogs as well, so, as was the routine when at home, it was the dogs that woke me up that morning in the van. They always came with us and were quite used to the change of environment, but dogs being pack animals, I think that they were a little restless, not having Ann and the kids there as well.

Golden Retrievers are big dogs and take up a great deal of space. In a caravan, space is at a premium, so you can imagine how they got in the way when there were two adults and a couple of kids there also. Ann wouldn't have it any other way though, so the dogs slept in the van.

I was vaguely aware of warm dog breath on my face, followed by the moist shammi-like sensation of a tongue licking my cheek. I opened my eyes and there was Mac looking into my face. Lear was still lying on the floor, but her face was turned up to mine. I extricated my right arm from the sleeping bag and ruffled the fur on the top of both dogs' heads.

As my sleep-drowsed senses cleared and I remembered where I was, I looked up to see if David was still asleep. Mac turned and padded in the direction of my gaze. David's nose protruded from the porthole in the hood of the sleeping bag. It was red and damp with perspiration and to a dog must have presented an irrisitable temptation. Mac began licking eagerly - David jumped, as one does when startled from sleep and fell from his bed to the floor. Mac, startled by this unexpected reaction, retreated to my end of the van.

It was then that began the fascinating and hilarious episode of David attempting to release himself from his bag.

As I mentioned at the beginning it reminded me of a butterfly, struggling to escape from its cocoon. As the bag had arms, David's hands were isolated from his body. The zip, which ran up the centre of the bag, was rather stiff and disinclined to open readily. I must confess that I'd half expected problems as David had insisted that I zip him in the night before and even with both hands, I'd had difficulty with it.

After several minutes' struggling, David's encapsulated form lay still. I was desperately trying to suppress my mirth. I heard him call my name softly. Had I tried to answer, however, I'm sure I'd have burst out laughing and I felt - perhaps rather cruelly - that there could be a lot more entertainment value in the situation. With David's tendency towards pomposity, I couldn't resist taking the opportunity of watching him sweat a little longer.

Again he called my name softly. I don't know why he felt it necessary to whisper - there was no one else in the van but me and there were only a handful of other vans on the site, most of which were on the opposite side of the field. I maintained my silence, but grinned hugely, hiding my face from him with the top of my own sleeping bag.

Then the wriggling started again. It was apparent from where I lay that he was trying to extract his arms from those of the bag, with the intention of reaching the inner tag of the zip. With a jumper or sweat shirt this is made possible by the stretchy nature of the fabric plus the fact that you have the use of your hands. Neither of these factors applied to this situation and it must have taken David nearly ten minutes of puffing and panting and a great deal of quiet cursing before he was finally able to achieve his goal. However, even with his one arm free, his problems were not yet over. As I've already said, the zip was extremely stiff and stubborn and no matter how David pulled and tugged at it, it refused to open more than two or three inches. With the draw-string still tied under his chin and being unable to release the knot with one hand (it had tightened with all of his exertions) David was faced with the prospect of either screaming for help, (something he seemed reluctant to do,) or extricating himself through an impossibly small opening.

I must confess that I was impressed by David's performance. I think Harry Houdini would have been. I doubt that David would have actually succeeded had the zip not finally surrendered and his body, soaked in sweat, red with exertion and panting hard from effort, burst forth at last. For me it was the final straw. I could contain myself no longer. I roared with laughter and, in the process, managed to fall off my own bed.

Breakfast over and the dishes washed it was time for the dogs' first walk of the day. The morning was glorious with not a hint of cloud in the sky. Even more surprising was the total lack of breeze.

The site on which the van was parked is in North Wales. It's on the coast, just brushing the Southern fringes of Snowdonia. It's a site that we've used on previous occasions for family holidays. The place is wonderful, the view inland, breath-taking. The mountains of the National Park, fill the picture window at the front of the van and the sea, although out of sight, is only a few hundred yards away behind high sand dunes. The beach, literally miles of unspoilt sand, is reached by a convenient board walk.

We set out, David, myself and the dogs. Lear and Mac, like all dogs, loved the beach. They knew it was there, just out of sight. Whether they remembered it from their last visit, or could smell the salt air, I'm not sure, but as soon as we were clear of the site and I let them off their leash, they both went bounding off towards the sea.

David had never been very comfortable around dogs. Like myself, he had not been brought up with them. He did, however, have a soft spot for my two. On previous occasions, when he and Kim had come to visit, he'd openly admitted deriving great pleasure from the long rambles that we'd taken together with Mac and Lear. He loved to watch them roaming around the woodland close to where we lived and where I walked them both daily. I wondered idly how he'd react seeing them on the shore. Anyone who has ever taken dogs on to a beach, (at least anyone that I've ever met,) always tells the same story. The effect of such a clear, unrestricted expanse of sand seems to create an almost universal surge of euphoric excitement on a dog's senses. Even elderly dogs, like our old dog Micky, would appear to revert to puppyhood when faced with such freedom. Mac and Lear were no exception.

By the time David and I topped the row of dunes, Mac and Lear were already gambolling about, chasing and cavorting with each other like spring lambs. As the sight of the apparently endless stretch of sand met David's eyes, I heard a distinct intake of breath. I'd seen this view on numerous occasions in the past, but even I was impressed by it that day. As I've already said, the sky was cloudless and the sun bright. Not a breath of wind stirred the marram grass that covered the high dunes. These conditions were most unusual for the coast. The sea, therefore, was like a sheet of glass, with only tiny wavelets lapping gently at the water's edge. I watched David's face intensely as he scanned the vista before him. His attention was suddenly diverted to the action centre-stage. Mac and Lear were charging about wildly. I noted, with quiet satisfaction, that a slight smile was playing at the corners of his mouth. Within a few seconds, his whole face broke into a broad grin. It was his first genuine smile since he'd arrived on our doorstep a few days previously.

We stepped from the board walk and crossed the soft dry sand at the top of the beach, making for the firmer, wet, tidal sand that was more easily walked on. As we started along the shore I ventured to ask, for the first time, about the problems that had brought him to our door, not, as I believed, simply for sanctuary, but for help. As Ann had gathered from Kim on the phone the problem had sprung from talk about starting a family.

David had never expressed an interest in becoming a father, at least not when we'd been closer. It appeared that his opinions had not changed. Kim, on the other hand, although initially disinterested, had suddenly realized that she was not getting any younger. As a result she'd suddenly "Gone broody" as David put it.

David, although not an only child, had a tendency to be a bit of a loner, (as I was myself) so I was, perhaps, able to identify with his feelings. I remember when Ann and I had first discussed the prospect of starting a family, I too had been reluctant to commit to a situation that would so irrevocably change the rest of our lives. Perhaps it's a male thing in general, but the prospect of such a total and inescapable commitment scared the life out of me. For me, though, that situation had arisen over a decade previously, when I was still in my twenties. David was in his late thirties and with middle age staring him firmly in the face, he'd become even more deeply entrenched in his male views. The strength of his feelings and, I'm afraid to say, his total intransigence on the subject meant that Kim's overwhelming maternal urges inevitably drove a wedge between them. Kim is one of the most patient people that I've ever met. David on the other hand, has great difficulty in expressing his full and innermost feelings even to her. This is not a problem, as a rule, as she can usually read him like a book. However with this situation where they were on totally opposite sides of the fence, David's failure to communicate had become an insuperable barrier.

As we walked along that morning, David would stop periodically to watch the dogs as they continued to gallop about madly. I suddenly realized that I'd never heard him talk so much and so openly before. I remember thinking that if he could have been as frank with Kim, then perhaps the problem would have resolved itself by now.

After about fifteen minutes' walking, we made our way to the foot of the dunes and sat on an old log. It was pitted and weathered - an oversized piece of drift-wood tossed up by some long past winter storm. David continued talking. The whole of his frustration, anger and sorrow spilled out on to the sand. I made little or no comment, reluctant to interrupt. I felt that it would be far better for him to get it out of his system. Even a burst dam empties and dries eventually though, and gradually David's flow slowed to a trickle.

Finally there came a long pause. I was just about to speak, wondering what I could possibly say to him, when he pointed towards the dogs and smiled. They had, by this time, slowed down a bit and were now rolling about in the soft sand, trying to bite each other's ears and tails. I grabbed what seemed to be an opportune moment to break in. I asked him if he'd ever considered owning a dog as it was apparent that he enjoyed the company of my two. He said that he had, but didn't think Kim would be overly keen on the idea. I asked if he'd ever suggested it to her. He paused and then confessed that he never actually had. I let this point sink in for a few seconds before adding that, of course, dogs were a big tie and knowing how he felt about kids, why should dogs be any different?

Again there was a long pause. He then asked if we'd ever thought about having them mated. I pointed out that, even if they hadn't been neutered, they were brother and sister. He seemed quite surprised that they'd been neutered and expressed sadness at the thought that they'd never fulfil themselves by producing a litter. They were such beautiful creatures! I stayed absolutely silent and, as I'd expected, the significance of his own remark sank in. For the second time that morning, his face exploded into a huge grin and he turned to look at me. "Am I really such a fool, my friend?" he said, still smiling. I pointed out that sometimes a little distance was all that was necessary to enable us to see things that were right under our nose.

He stood up and walked over to where the dogs were now lying panting - spent after their exertions. He sat down on the sand between them and, extending an arm to each, gave them a huge fuss in a way that I'd never seen him do before. Mac and Lear would let anyone fuss them and lolled back all over him, vying for even more attention.

A short time later we began to stroll back the way we had come. All the way, David talked about, and asked questions concerning my own children. He'd always been very good with Jamie and Beth, a point that had not escaped me and which I pointed out to him. Some of his questions were really quite considered, while others were trivial - a reflection of his still deep-rooted doubts and fears at the prospect of fatherhood - the real crux of the problem. Up to that point David's life had been extremely ordered. Because he was rather lazy, he made sure that every element of his life which might cause him undue work or hardship was either side stepped or organized in such a way as to be of as little trouble to him as possible. Children would most certainly make his life unbelievably difficult at times; a point that I made absolutely no bones about. However, I also assured him that the pleasure derived from having kids, in my opinion, far out-weighed any hardships. You cannot really explain or describe to anyone who has no experiences of parenthood, what it's really like - mainly because it's different for everyone.

All the way back David would break off to throw pieces of driftwood for the dogs to fetch. He was amused by their tireless diligence in retrieving whatsoever he threw for them- also the fierce competition between the two animals to reach their target first - the proud victor bearing it back for him to throw again.

Just up the road from the caravan site was a telephone box - the old red variety. David was eager, yet nervous, at the prospect of speaking to Kim. Not surprisingly, he feared that his unreasonable behaviour might possibly have caused an unbridgeable gap between them.

I felt sure that, were he to speak to Kim and try to explain everything, she would be only too pleased to listen. If there was one thing that I had absolutely no doubt about, it was that Kim loved David very deeply and I felt sure she would be longing to talk to him.

Not wanting to be intrusive, I went back to the van while David made his call. However, he was back at the van before I'd even got a kettle to boil. His face was as long as it had been when he'd first turned up. "No reply" he said. I suggested that perhaps she'd gone shopping. Ann quite often went out to the shops if she was low. David seemed convinced that she would have been there and would not believe anything other than the worst. I suddenly had a flash of inspiration. "Forget the tea" I said, "Come with me." I practically dragged him back to the phone box. I left him outside, holding the dogs and dialled my home number. I heard the receiver being picked up and then Ann's voice answering. I had a few brief words with her, all the time watching the sad and dejected figure of my old friend through the grimy, salt-caked glass panels, as he half-heartedly stroked the dogs.

After about a minute's conversation with Ann I pushed open the door and held out the phone in David's direction. "Come and speak to your wife" I said. "She's at our house." His face was an absolute picture of relief mixed with nervous tension as he took the receiver from me. I told him I'd see him at the van and started back down the road. Just before I turned into the site, I glanced back at the phone box. I could just make out David inside. The elbow of his free hand was resting on top of the coin box and his head was cradled in his palm. Well, I thought, it's up to you now, mate!

It was nearly an hour before he finally returned and, thank God, there was a smile on his face. He came into the van and sat down. The dogs nuzzled around him, inviting the attention that he freely gave. "Well?" I said, "Well," he replied, "of course, there's still a great deal to talk about, but we both think it would be nice for our children to grow up with dogs in the house." I smiled. "I suppose we'd better think about heading home then." "No rush," he replied, "Ann said that she and Kim were off clothes-shopping to spend all our money."
"Oh, wonderful!" I said.

In From The Cold

Warm dark fluid sanctuary
Constant beating soothes and
   comforts.
Pressure builds, moves me down,
Squeezing tighter, tighter,
Bursting forth,
Bright light, dazzling light,
Shivering cold, shaking fear.
Something near, shadow falls,
Tongue caressing, soothing,
   reassuring,
Mother!

Must rise, need to rise
Lifting, lifting, stumbling, falling.
Try again, steady, steady,
Must stay up.
Falter, step,
Stagger, step.
Walking!

Gnawing hunger, Need to feed.
Calling, calling. There below.
Sucking, sucking,
Warm sweet liquid, going down.
Hunger fading,
Comfort, safe, secure.

Mother lies, not moving, Not rising.
Lying close for warmth.
Something wrong.
Feel the faltering rise and fall,
Hear the soft beating, slowing,
   slowing,
Stop.
Final rise,
Final fall,
Falling, falling away to nothing,
Still.

Cold dread,

Lonely, so lonely.

Shouting, shouting,

Shout my fear,

My chill,

My empty despair.

Biting hunger.

Weary sleep creeping up.

Tall shadow moving close,

Want to run,

Want to hide.

Too weak, too tired.

Arms reach down,

Grasp me,

Wrap me.

Wrap me warm,

Wrap me tight.

Rising up, lifted high,

Moving swiftly.

Held firmly.

Carried far,

Carried long.

Enter in.

Dark still air.

Strange smells all around.

Laid down,

Gently, gently.

No grass, no wind,

Yet soft below me.

Hot flickering glow, warms and
   comforts.
Fear subsides.
Dark shape moves out from the
   shadow
Mother! mother!
Lies down beside me.
Soft fur,
Warm breath on my face,
Sooths and reassures.
Strange scent, not mother!
Feel the rise and fall once more,
Hear the soft beat again.

Tall shape appears once more,
Bending over, arm outstretched.
Something strange in my mouth.
Is it?
Yes, yes.
Sucking hard, sucking fast.
Feel the warm familiar fluid,
Running down,
Filling up.
Feel safe, Feel full,
Feel content.
Relaxing, sleepy, sleepy.
Soft body beside me.
Sanctuary.

Young Highlanders

Towards the end of 1994, my wife, Sue, decided that she wanted another dog of her own. At the time our two current dogs, Jessie and Martha were about ten years old. Ironically, when we had acquired them at eight weeks old, the intention was that Martha would be Sue's and Jessie mine. However, dogs have a habit of gravitating towards one specific family member and in a very short space of time both dogs attached themselves firmly to me. This did not prove a problem for Sue as they were still very much family pets and much loved by all. Since her old dog Mick had departed, eight years previously, much of Sue's attention had been taken up with our two children, Jamie and Beth. We also had a number of cats for which Sue, especially, has a passion.

Inevitably, the time came when Sue felt that she wanted a dog of her own again. She had expressed an interest in West Highland Terriers. A small dog, she felt, would be more suited to her lifestyle.

It just so happened that at that time, Sue's mother was also thinking about acquiring a new dog. They decided that they would look together.

The end result was the two characters you see in the picture. The one sitting is Charley (my mother-in-law's) and the cheeky chappy lying beside him is Berkley, our dog, or to be correct I should say, Sue's.

Like all puppies they were adorable and, inevitably, I soon got the urge to paint them. They were about four months old when I started the picture that you see and, at that stage, resembled walking mop-heads rather than dogs. Not surprisingly, despite their genetic origins, they had never been to Scotland. However, I felt that a background which suggested The Highlands would be appropriate. The manipulation of the elements within a composition is one of the many advantages and delights of painting. So to create an image of two such young pups, apparently nestling amongst the heather and rocks of a Scottish moor, gave me a great deal of pleasure.

It was very shortly after I had completed "Young Highlanders" that Sue had Berkley clipped for the first time. By then we had all grown used to him looking like a teddy bear, indeed, he was affectionately known by us all as "Berkley Bear." The prospect of having all his fur cut off filled Sue, especially, with some apprehension.

On the day that we had him trimmed I have to admit that even I was a little nervous. Upon arriving to collect him we were presented with a new dog. The Berkley Bear whom we had all come to know and love had vanished. Before us was the most adorable little creature whose appearance had more in common with a spring lamb than a teddy bear.

The psychological effect of delivering one dog and collecting another was quite profound and it occurred to me that everyone who has ever owned a Westie must have gone through this experience at some point.

With barely a week left before the "Young Highlanders" picture was due to be published, I hurriedly sketched and painted Berkley as he now looked and showed the resulting image to Glyn, my publisher. He decided that this small study entitled "First Clip" should be printed with the main picture and be presented as a companion piece to "Young Highlanders."

It is perhaps ironic that despite the disproportionate amount of work in the two pieces, it is "First Clip" that has generated the most interest and I think that this clearly illustrates that it is not necessarily the pictures which involve hours of work and fine detail that grab the public's attention. The simplest images are quite often the most effective.

Just as a footnote I should like to point out that Berkley has turned out to be everything that Sue had hoped for. He is totally devoted to her and follows her wherever she goes. He is loving and affectionate and needs to be close, indeed he is rather like Mary's lamb from the nursery rhyme. Coincidentally, Sue's middle name is Mary.

Yours Faithfully

I was just six weeks old when you came into my life and from that day on you have cared for me.

When I cried in the dark you came to me and gave me comfort
When I was hungry you fed me
When I was cold you made me warm
When I needed to run you gave me trees and grass
When I needed love you gave it freely and with affection.

I will never question or ask you why
When you need me I will be there
When you speak I will listen
When you command I will obey
If you are threatened I will defend you.

Whatever you say, whatever you do, whether you whisper or whether you shout, whether you show affection or displeasure, I shall never betray or desert you. I will always remain, yours faithfully.

Now and Then

It's exactly fifteen years to the day since the old plough turned its last furrow. It was the same day that Jessie was born and the reason I remember is because it was also my sixth birthday.

Jessie's been a wonderful dog. She's one of those dogs that never really needed training, she just seemed to pick up all that was required of her and get on with it, without fuss or nonsense. Mind you, she had the best teachers. Her father Jack, and my grandfather, Grandpa Clem, had won several prizes for working sheep at the county show and so I guess it was in the blood.

My Grandfather was a traditionalist. He loathed modern practices and stuck tenaciously to the old ways. He had been retired officially for many years by the time I was born (my mother had me late in life and I think I came as a bit of a surprise). Even so, Grandpa Clem would still help out on the farm. However, he refused point blank to have anything to do with modern machinery. For him, horse power was the only true way. As a result, my father kept a wonderful team of magnificent shires called Bill and Ben, so enabling his father to 'play with his toys' as my dad put it.

My earliest and most enduring memory of Grandpa Clem was the image of him silhouetted against an evening sky in spring, cresting the top field, his great hands grasping the plough handles firmly with Bill and Ben, their powerful bodies straining forward to drive the share through the top soil and cast it over.

On that eventful day fifteen years ago, the old plough finally gave up the ghost and broke beyond repair. Grandpa Clem left it to rust behind the old barn and there it lies to this day. That evening, he received a message from his friend and neighbour, Fred Little, that their bitch Millie had given birth to four pups and as Jack was the father, would Clem like to have the pick of the litter. This must have been some consolation to Grandpa Clem after the loss of the plough, and that is how we came to have Jessie.

Of course, as all this occurred on my birthday, I was far too preoccupied to really care. It was some years later that the day's events came back to me clearly.

Grandpa Clem passed away about ten tears ago now. My father sold Bill and Ben to a working farm museum. He also gave them all of Grandpa's 'toys' as well, but the old plough remained, almost as an epitaph to both my Grandfather and the way that things once were.

Jessie is, of course, retired now but on sunny days you can still find her lying by the remains of the plough, apparently day dreaming, perhaps recalling those by-gone times. Incidentally, I'm twenty-one years old today. Maybe this is an appropriate day to look back myself and remember, before turning and looking to the future.

Over and Under

There is a hush upon the wood. A stillness so intense, it seems to have substance. Thick snow, virginal in its unsullied white purity, blankets not only the woodland floor, but sound itself. The calm is cathedral-like, a feeling enhanced by the trees, their great trunks rising skywards like mighty stone pillars, supporting a fan-vaulted ceiling - a canopy of bough branch and twig. The slightest breeze would stir and rattle this lattice-work vault, but the morning is breathless and everything is motionless as if carved from living rock.

The early sun, diluted by morning mist, shoots pallid beams of light and warmth which pierce and penetrate the woodland realm. The air-born particles of moisture reflect and refract in the ethereal shafts and make them appear almost tangible.

A mighty beech, veteran of nearly two hundred years, which finally succumbed to disease and high winds, lies prone across a woodland path, its swan-song to life a few meagre green shoots in spring.

The path, a highway and byway for woodland inhabitants, bears no trace of hoof or paw as the cold snap is a deterrent to most who would travel that way.

Far off, beyond sight, a sudden staccato cry fractures the silence. A cock-pheasant, disturbed at the outer-fringes of the wood, rockets skyward. The urgency conveyed in his wing-clap and call, warns all of intruders.

At the first sounds of the invader's approach, the wood seems to hold its breath in anticipation. Carried faintly but clearly on the chill morning air is the unmistakeable crisp and crunch of rapid footfalls on frosted snow. Then, like the appropriate melody to the percussion of running feet, there comes the snuffling, panting breath of excitement and exertion.

Like whirlwinds they appear. Their life, their vitality and energy seem magnified by the deathly stillness of the stage upon which their drama unfolds. The rapid exhalations of spent air, warm and moist from lungs, explodes from their nostrils and gaping mouths in steamy clouds.

The older dog, liver and white, chooses to search beneath the fallen tree. The slightest hint, the merest suggestion of a scent, may permeate up from under the snow and if so, his keen nose will detect it.

His younger companion, black and white and just out of puppyhood, is still more concerned with play than the serious pursuit of scents and smells. To her the old beech is a bridge - a mighty wooden arch spanning the path below - something new to explore and conquer - something to be jumped on and over.

Suddenly, from far off, like distant rifle reports echoing through the trees, two names are called, sharply. Immediately there follows a long single note, so faint and high-pitched as to be almost inaudible.

To the dogs' ears, however, it is clear and distinct. An undeniable call that must be obeyed!

As if synchronized, both heads snap to attention, ears pricked and alert to the summons. In that briefest of moments, the two creatures are motionless, as frozen as the world around them. Then, with bounding strides, they are gone - vanished from sight.

The sound of racing feet and rasping breath fades and quiet returns, but, like the ghosts of a former presence, the paws that punctured and stirred the pristine snow have left their mark; their impressions like scars on milky-white skin. From the distant edge of the wood come two faint barks, a final farewell from departing travellers. Then, as if someone had drawn a quilt over the trees, peace descends and a hush settles once more upon the wood.

Last of the Summer Wine

It's still dark when the farmer rises, even in early Spring. He quickly slips on trousers, shirt and a heavy jumper against the chill of the bedroom air, his breath coming in steamy clouds. His wife, a nondescript hump beneath the bedclothes, stirs and mumbles to her husband. He grunts in reply and leaves the room. As he does so, two shapes that have lain curled and silent together in the far corner, rise with gently swinging tails and follow their master through the door.

Downstairs, in the kitchen, the farmer tip-toes across a cold quarry-tiled floor in stockinged feet. His first task of the morning, is to open the fire door of the old stove and stir life into the embers. Then, throwing on a couple of logs from the pile in the corner, he takes the kettle from its shelf and fills it at the sink before returning to the stove and placing it on the heat.

While he waits for the kettle to sing, he takes bread from the pantry which he slices and butters. Sitting at the table that occupies the centre of the room, he signals to his two companions. They have waited patiently for this moment, watching their master's daily routine, anticipating his sign. They scurry to him, their eagerness causing their claws to scratch and scrape on the worn ceramic floor. Sitting before him, bolt upright, eyes fixed on the treat held in the master's hand, the younger dog raises his paw and places it on the man's lap. The farmer tears the buttered round in two and giving the command, "Be gentle," gives the two animals their reward.

Having made and drunk his tea - after struggling into overalls and donning and lacing his old work boots - the farmer opens the kitchen door and steps outside, prepared to face the day. He whistles, but only one dog follows, across the yard, through the gate and away down the lane. It is the young dog that departs, for the old girl, his mother, has done with work. Now, she idles her days away around the farm house, while her son carries out the duties that she once performed.

She settles on the step by the door, to take in the sights, sounds and smells that the new day offers her. Above the roof of the barn, the sky is stained pink and the few ribbons of cloud that adorn it have their lower edges gilded by the morning's first shafts of sunlight.

It is Spring and the dawn chorus is well under way; the many varieties of birds, both large and small, proclaiming their territorial rights to all who will listen. Amongst the myriad songs of finch, lark, pippet and thrush, the old bitch picks out the croonings of pigeons and doves. A pheasant's cry drifts across the pastures from the edge of the wood, while the squabbling chatter of house sparrows in the eaves above her head signals the start of yet another dispute between these argumentative little creatures.

It is her nose that warns her of her master's imminent return. Her sense of smell, although dulled by the passage of years, is still many times more acute than any human's. Carried on the slight morning breeze is just a hint - the merest suggestion - of the pungent odour of cows. Then her one good ear catches the first audible sounds of the milk herd's approach. The soft lowing and the rattle of many hooves on tarmac heralds its arrival.

The farmer appears at the gate to usher the lead animals into the yard, while the young dog harries and drives the stragglers at the rear. His job is to ensure that none are distracted from their progress by the lush spring grass that fringes the narrow lane.

The thirty or so cows, that make up the farmer's modest herd, file slowly into the yard. The milking parlour is small and holds just a handful of animals at one time, but, like all gregarious creatures, there is a hierarchy. The most senior cows, conditioned by their twice daily routine, enter first of their own accord.

As the hum and throb of the milking machine starts up in the shed, the young dog trots across the yard and sits by his mother. His services temporarily redundant, he relaxes and the two dogs casually observe the throng of black and white that mills aimlessly around the yard, waiting patiently for their turn to enter the parlour. Here they'll have the four sucking cups fitted that will draw away the mounting pressure in their sagging udders.

The number of waiting beasts gradually diminishes as the farmer completes the first job of the day. The cows that have been milked are sent out through a rear door to a paddock behind the parlour. Here they wait, once more, to be returned to their field.

Milking completed, the farmer whistles the young dog to drive the herd back down the lane. The old dog is left alone on the step once again.

With the departure of the cows, peace descends on the farm. A few of the resident hens appear from in and around the various out-buildings that skirt the yard. Always wary of the herd's many clumsy feet, they reappear, as if by magic, the moment the last cows have gone. With slow, apparently hesitant steps and lowered heads, they start to scour the dirt for specks of food and grit of which only they seem aware. The convulsive jerks of heads and necks as they feed cause the livid red wattles that adorn their crowns to flap from side to side, while they emit soft, soothing croonings that seem to emanate from deep within their plump round bodies.

From inside the farm house, as well, there are signs of activity. The farmer's wife has risen and set about cooking breakfast. The sound of slippers shuffling on the tiled floor, the rattle of the frying pan on the stove and water running in the sink are accompanied by what is, to the old dog, the best part of breakfast time - the heavenly aroma of bacon as it sizzles and spits in the pan.

Shortly afterwards the master returns. As he enters the house, he stoops briefly and casually pats the old dog's head. The younger dog approaches his mother and licks her mouth in greeting. She rises and follows them both into the kitchen.

Breakfast passes with its regular tit-bit treats of bacon rind and toast crusts and the farmer, having eaten heartily, returns to his work. He loads a trailer with hay bales, fence posts and barbed wire, then disappears into the barn. Here he keeps the old tractor, a great blue monster that's seen better days. The farmer doesn't use it much any more, as its reliability is questionable. So it spends most of its time standing idle in a corner of the barn, where it slowly grows older and drips oil on the straw below its sump.

There are several dry coughs and a sigh from its diesel engine, a pause, several more coughs and the tractor throbs into life. The two dogs, still on the step, watch the cloud of blue-grey smoke that billows from the open doors of the barn. Then, like a mighty blue charger galloping out through the smoke of battle, the old tractor sallies forth from its stable. The farmer, astride his great steed, bounces about almost comically. The large springs on which the primitive metal seat is mounted, cause him to bob and sway like a Jack in the Box.

Hitching up the trailer, the man whistles his young dog once more. With one nimble bound he's up and the old rig trundles out of the farm yard. The young dog settles himself amongst the bales and seems to glance back at his mother in a gesture of farewell.

The rumble and chug of the diesel fades as the noisy machine heads off for the high pastures. Long after its departure though and when its din has diminished to silence, the old dog's nose still detects traces of its acrid fumes and hot oil.

The morning is fresh after the early chill, but the clear blue April sky holds the promise of spring warmth later. The long shadows of morning that blanket the yard, subduing the light and temperature, slowly retreat as the sun at last peeps shyly above the roof of the barn. As its brilliant orb arcs slowly upwards and across, its golden light bathes first the roof, then the walls of the milking parlour opposite, finally kissing the ground, where it creeps imperceptibly, yet inexorably, towards the spot where the old dog lies. As her body is enveloped in light and warmth, she raises her head and, squinting her eyes against the glare, draws in a great breath which she releases in a long sigh. The pledge of re-birth that Spring bestows stirs the blood and invigorates even her old bones.

As the morning slips easily towards noon and the sun approaches its zenith, the old dog remains, still and relaxed, on the step. With eyes closed and ears flat she gives the appearance of sleep, but far off, from the high pastures where her master and son work diligently, there drifts the occasional distant throb of the tractor, punctuated periodically by the faint report of an excited bark. As these familiar audible snippets reach her prostrate form, her good ear twitches and rises to catch every available trace of sound and one eye opens a fraction.

Before the morning is done the farmer's wife appears in the door way, her arms cradling a linen basket loaded with damp sheets and shirts. The heavy, steam-laden air of the kitchen, laced with the fragrance of soap, spills out as the door opens and she emerges. She walks round to the side of the house where a small area of grass, fenced off from the yard, sports a single ancient pear tree, twisted and crippled with age. Strung from the side of the house by a rusty iron hook and spanning the grass to a post on the far side, is the washing line. The old dog follows his mistress round and settles herself in the dappled shade of the pear tree's spindly limbs. She watches with idle curiosity as the farmer's wife methodically pegs out the various articles. The large sheets, milk-white and translucent, form screens on which her buxom form, full and round, is cast in silhouette by the back light of the sun, her arms outstretched above her head as she levels and pegs them to the line. Having completed the task, she takes a long wooden prop that lies by the farm house wall. Slotting the middle of the line into a groove at one end of the prop she hoists its contents high to catch the breeze. Then, lifting the now empty basket, she makes her way back to the kitchen and disappears inside. The old dog rises and follows, but declines the mistress' invitation to enter and settles herself once more on the step.

Some time later, when noon has passed and the sun has begun its steady dip towards the horizon, the old dog detects the racket of the tractor in the lane and soon it appears, roaring and rattling into the farm yard. The master still dances about on its over-sprung seat and the young dog - the hay bales no longer aboard the trailer - rides the chassis, just behind the master. His mouth is open wide and his tongue lolls limply to one side as he pants to cool the heat of exertion.

The man and his dogs enter the house. Having completed the washing, the farmer's wife has prepared lunch - a light affair of cold meat, pickles and pork pie. Again the dogs are spoilt with tasty morsels and scraps from the master's plate.

By mid-afternoon, the farmer is back at work. Although the shadows have now begun to draw back across the yard, the warmth of the day is only just reaching its peak and the farmer is down to shirt sleeves, an old cloth cap still sitting resolutely upon his balding head, like a badge of office. It's rarely discarded, even at the height of summer.

He disappears into the barn to where the tractor has now been returned. For the next two hours he tinkers with its geriatric engineering. Outside, on the step, the two dogs lie together listening to the clink and clunk of spanner and wrench as their master tries to inject further life into his faithful old retainer.

The mistress appears, a bag of grain in her arms for the chickens. She chortles and clucks to call the scattered poultry to her. This - another of the farm's daily routines - brings the hungry birds running to her from every conceivable direction, until there are about twenty hens milling about her feet. With broad sweeps of her arm she scatters the grains in wide arcs. The crooning and chatter of the chickens rises in volume as the excitement of food has them running wildly about, struggling and squabbling in groups where the seeds fall to the ground. The woman, having dispensed the fodder, returns to her kitchen, while the commotion she has stirred in the yard gradually dies down as the hens' initial exuberance subsides into their more usual routine. The dogs look on with indifference from the step.

As afternoon races towards evening, the farmer departs once more, calling the young dog to him as he leaves. It is time for the evening milking. The old dog still watches as the morning's procedure is repeated. The milling herd in the yard, that gradually reduces in number, the hum and chug of machinery from the parlour and the all pervading odour of bovine dung and urine that assails the dogs' keen noses.

The yard is again blanketed in shadow when master and dog return from the cow pasture and the chill of evening nips the air. At the open kitchen door, the man unties and removes his boots. He turns and calls softly to the old girl still lying on the step. She looks up adoringly into her master's face, rises stiffly and enters. Behind her the door shuts for the last time.

Wish You Were Here

The garden hasn't been the same since Grandad passed away. In later years he'd spent most of his time out there. Even when it rained, he'd be busy in his potting shed. Then on those long summer evenings, he'd sit on his favourite bench, at the bottom of the garden, with old Ben curled at his feet, surveying his handiwork. Ben was like his shadow - never leaving his side.

Old Ben is still with us. His muzzles's grey and his back legs aren't what they were but he still plods on.

I don't go down the garden very often these days, but that old bench is still there and whenever I see it, it's like an old nostalgic tune, bringing it all back. Just the other day I was down there with Ben; the sun was low at the day's end and just for one brief moment I thought I caught the scent of pipe smoke.

Seven Up

Dear Sarah,

First of all, allow me to apologise for not writing sooner but the last few months have been rather hectic, as I shall outline, but here I am at last!

It was wonderful to receive your last letter and Sue and I are so pleased that you, Bob and the kids are settling down and fitting in so well. It's hard to believe that it's nearly two years since you emigrated and I must confess I wasn't sure how well you'd adjust. Australia's so different and so far away, but I am genuinely thrilled that it all seems to be working out for you. My big sister, an Aussie! Hard to believe!

Well, the news.
A couple of weeks before your letter arrived, (about the middle of March,) we finally lost our old dog Harry. You can imagine what effect this had on Sue, but I was surprised at how upset I felt myself at his passing.

As you know, Mom and Dad never allowed us big pets when we were young, so when I married Sue, it took a little time to adjust to dog ownership. It probably didn't help that Harry was already mature by the time Sue and I took the plunge and I think it must have been as unsettling for Harry as it was for me when I first moved in.

I feel sure that Mark and James will also be saddened by the news, as my most enduring memories of both Harry and the boys were those weekends in the summer of 1992, when you, Bob, Mark and James came to stay. Do you remember how hot it was, that one weekend in August? We spent the whole of Saturday and most of Sunday sitting on the terrace, drinking beer and lemonade. You and Bob talked about your plans for Australia, while the boys spent their time running around the meadow in their swimming trunks and playing with Harry. They'd run in and out of the stream at the bottom, getting covered in mud and having the time of their lives and they probably felt much cooler than us stuffy grown-ups.

As you know, Sue and I have been trying to start a family ourselves for some time now and our apparent inability to get the show on the road prompted us to have some tests done. The outcome of this only proved that there was nothing wrong with either of us. This seemed to make things worse for Sue. As the doctor put it, "The wish is barring the way." What he was saying was that we were trying too hard. "Try to be more relaxed about the whole thing." That seemed to be his best advice.

The loss of Harry at this time did nothing to help the situation, especially for Sue. Desperately wanting a baby, Harry had become even more important to her.

Then your letter arrived. You'd have thought that your news of Bob's promotion, the boys' success at school and of course your own good fortune on the job front, would have made Sue almost suicidal.

If you add to the fact that we were buried under several inches of snow, while you were basking in temperatures in the high eighties, I nearly didn't show the letter to her at all! To my complete and utter surprise, it had exactly the reverse effect, it seemed to actually lift her spirits. It was at this point that I had my brain-wave - get another dog. A puppy!

I found out from a mate at work, that there was a litter of Labrador puppies at a farm some fifteen miles from here. Well, you know Sue's passion for Labs. That convinced me that I was doing the right thing. I decided not to tell Sue what I was up to. I thought it would be a nice surprise for her and (just in case things didn't work out,) she wouldn't be disappointed. The last thing I wanted to do was add to her depression.

The place was called Brecon Heath Farm and the farmer's name Jones. I looked up the number and gave him a call. It turned out that there were seven pups in the litter, of which three were still available. I made an appointment and, making my excuses to Sue, I snuck over there one evening.

The farm was small and by no means modern. Most of the barns and out-buildings looked in need of repair. Mr Jones looked at least as old as the farm and could have done with a little restoration himself.

He led me into one of the barns, which appeared to be the most substantial of them all. It was dark inside, but when my eyes had adjusted and, with the aid of some rather cracked and grimy windows, I was aware of Mr Jones in the far corner kneeling by what appeared to be an old door - propped on its side - across the mouth of a small recess. I was suddenly aware of a scratching and rustling sound, accompanied by the unmistakeable whines and whimpers of puppies. As I peered over the old door and into the gloom beyond, my heart was instantly lost to the sight that greeted me. A yellow bitch was lying on her side in the straw and in the dim light, there appeared to be a seething, writhing mass of black fur sprouting from beneath her. The only exception to the black was one patch of lighter fur squirming with the rest. It was the only discernible puppy-shape amongst the mêlée. "Six black and one yellow," said Mr Jones. "Funny thing nature, isn't it?" Mr Jones is a man of few words.

Having allowed the puppies to finish feeding, the old farmer proceeded to lift three of the litter out from behind the old door, two black and the yellow pup, I expressed my surprise that the yellow one was still available "Not so popular with the sporting folk as the black." Was his rather curt answer.

The puppies were barely four weeks old and as I watched them scrambling around in the deep straw, I suddenly realized how different in appearance they were from each other. Even at that tender age and allowing for the obvious difference in colour, there were distinct facial characteristics.

I had to make up my mind, so I picked them up one at a time. I tell you, Sarah, they were all so appealing! I was tempted to take them all. However, I had to choose one.

The first one I picked up was black. He had a slightly puggish appearance and suddenly I was transported back to the old sweet shop in the High Street at Sheldon, where we grew up. Do you remember, Sarah, how we'd drop in on our way to school in the morning, with the pennies we'd saved from our pocket-money? You'd hold my hand and we'd buy four of those liquorice sweets each - you know, the ones with the little black smiling face on the wrapper. We'd have one straight away, one at the break in the morning, one at lunch time and one walking home from school. That way, they'd last all day. That was the theory anyway. You always seemed to manage it, but mine were usually all gone before break.

Do you recall the old lady that owned the sweet shop? Ma Dillon. I tell you, that puppy could have been her. Do you remember how she'd stand behind the counter, watching us like a hawk, making us feel like mice about to be eaten? That flat nose, the tight pursed lips and those round bulging eyes that she never took off you for an instance. Russell Green used to say that she reminded him of a stupid dog. Stupid dogs have flat noses and bulging eyes, because they always chase parked cars. The vision of Ma Dillon running into the back of a stationary car still brings a smile to my lips today and it was with that thought that I put the first puppy down. I picked up the second pup - the other black one. His face was sharper and less wrinkled.

Do you remember Colin Smith at school? He was a year above me and one below you. He was also the school bully. There was one occasion in the playground, when for some reason I'd got on the wrong side of him. He had me pinned in a corner and was pushing and prodding me. He was only a little chap and perhaps had it just been him and me, I might have had a go but, as usual, he had his "gang" with him so I felt totally helpless and humiliated. I remember feeling tears rising up uncontrollably, and hard as I tried to suppress them, they came welling up. I wasn't hurt, as I recall, just intimidated. There was I, curled up in a ball, sobbing quietly while Smith and his crew bent over me laughing and jeering.

The next thing I remember was a gap appearing in the heads above me. Then a hush fell and bodies around me parted like the Dead Sea. As the gap widened, I looked up and saw you, Sarah. With your face as black as thunder, you looked like Moses, marching resolutely through the divided throng. You bent down and gently helped me to my feet. By this time your anger was approaching boiling point. You turned on Smithy and, as I recall, you were even smaller than him, but the volley upon volley of insults and abuse that you fired at him, were wonderful to hear. I can still visualize that smug grin that always seemed to adorn his pointed features, slowly fade away to what can only be described as shell-shock. Needless to say, he later tried to laugh it off, but I don't think his image and status ever fully recovered from the verbal barrage that you laid on him that day - in front of the whole school as well. At any rate, he never bothered me again.

I put down the second puppy and turned to the third and final little character - the yellow one. Before I picked her up, I knelt down in the straw beside her. Immediately she jumped up and snuggled into my lap. As she lay there she turned her head up towards me and looked into my face. I know you'll probably laugh, Sarah, but it was Nan's face. Do you remember how she'd look at us when we were getting out of hand? She'd never scold or shout, she'd just look at us with an expression of infinite patience and that was enough to have the desired effect. To this day, I can't really fathom out how she managed it. Had it been Mom or Dad, we'd probably have gone on pushing our luck until the wrath of God had descended on us, but never with Nan. So that was that - the decision was made - no contest! It had to be the little yellow one.

Shortly after that, Sue tentatively suggested that things might have started to happen. We did a couple of home tests, both of which were inconclusive. Those home-test kits are supposed to be fool-proof, but I think the manufacturers had slightly more gifted fools in mind when they designed them. We therefore decided to go to hospital and let the professionals handle it.

The hospital visit was last week, just a day before I was due to pick up the puppy, of which Sue still knew nothing. We were told that due to problems at the lab, it would take about a week to get the results. You can imagine what a strain that would have been for both of us, particularly Sue, but turning up the following evening with a puppy, could not have been better timed if I'd actually planned it. Sue's face was an absolute picture of surprise and delight when I walked in with her.

You remember how I said the puppy's face reminded me of Nan's? Well, I told Sue about it and, as a result, we've decided to call the puppy "Ellie," short for Elsie, Nan's middle name.

I'm writing this having just mopped up a rather large puddle from under the kitchen table - just one of the many delights of raising a pup. We still haven't heard from the hospital, but expect to at any time. I'm going to sign off now, Sarah, as I think I can smell something unpleasant from the direction of the kitchen. Despite all the hard work Ellie is a poppet and as well as the pleasure she's brought Sue, I think I'm going to get something special from knowing her.

Give my love to all, take care of yourselves and as soon as there's any news I'll phone.

Lots of love,
Philip.

P.S. As I was about to seal the envelope, the phone rang. It was the hospital. Congratulations Aunty! Looks like the dog and I are going to become very close friends.

Ladies in Waiting

This painting has the distinction of being the only one in the book that has not been published as a limited edition print. However, I could not possibly have omitted it from a collection such as this.

It is a typical "Nigel Hemming Narrative Image." I would even go so far as to suggest that it is a rather pleasing picture. Nevertheless, these are not the reasons that I insisted on its inclusion in the book. It is because these are my dogs, Jessie and Martha.

It has been said that you always remember your first dog with the greatest affection. As Jessie and Martha are <u>my</u> first dogs and, (although getting on in years,) are still with me, I have no others with which to compare them. However, they are such wonderful characters that I cannot imagine any other dogs ever surpassing them in my esteem.

The image, I believe, speaks for itself. Like the picture "Anticipation" also in this book, anyone who has ever had anything to do with dogs will know that at the same time every day dogs get restless. Dogs are creatures of habit, and most of them are walked daily at the same times. As a result, they usually sense that time before you do and if you don't show the appropriate signs of preparation, they'll let you know in no uncertain terms. To be honest, when I first conceived and painted this picture, the dogs were actually looking at the door. It was intended to depict the anticipated arrival of a family member.

Before my wife, Sue, and I got married, she had a wonderful Sheltie dog named Micky. Like her present dog, Berkley, Micky was devoted to her. At the time, Sue worked for the family business in Birmingham. Every night of the week she would arrive home at about the same time and every night, Micky would go to the front room window and sit on a chair, watching the driveway for his mistress' imminent arrival. He would always be there waiting when she pulled up on the drive.

When I had finished the picture, there were a number of adverse comments from several people to the effect that you could not see the dogs' faces. I must confess, however, that it was not until I discussed the picture with my publisher, Glyn, who was considering printing the image and who also expressed similar concerns, that I seriously thought about changing the picture.

The result was the painting that you see illustrated. For various reasons it was never published and the original now hangs in pride of place over our fireplace at home. (Well let's face it, I could hardly allow anyone else to own a painting of my girls, now could I?)

I do think it's of some interest, nevertheless, that by the simple expediency of turning the girls' heads around, the theme of expectancy within the picture, has shifted from anticipating an imminent arrival, to be waiting to be taken out.

At the end of the day, the only thing that really matters to me is that it's a picture of my girls. Something that will endure beyond their departure. It's a time that I dread, for they mean so much to me and I love them both dearly.

In Retirement

I lie with heavy head on weary limbs and watch my master depart. The young dog, with jaunty step, trots at his heels his head held high with pride and youthful conceit.

At the gate he pauses briefly and glances back in my direction. A flicker of pity seems to dance across his coal-black features. Then with a cocky wag of his tail he vanishes from sight - but not from mind - for they follow a path that I know of old - a road I took many times before he had even stirred in his mother's womb.

Halfway down the lane is the old stump. He will pause there for his nose to read the messages, old and new, that permeate the rotting wood. Then he will cock his leg to say, "I was here." But I was there before him. I remember when it was not a stump but a tree, a great soaring oak. I remember the night it was struck by lightening and fell, but to him it was just an old stump, somewhere to leave his mark and move on.

At the bottom of the lane is a gate which leads to fields. These are the great open stretches of grass where a young dog can be given his head, where he can run and play.

The morning dew, a silvery sheen that blankets the green, shimmers in the early light. A myriad of tiny droplets glinting and glistening, bejewel each blade of grass like winter frost.

Here he will run and bound as if unleashed for the first time. The feeling of open space is too much for his young blood to resist. When his initial exuberance has passed, he'll quarter the field - nose to the ground - following the scent trails that criss-cross the damp earth, invisible to the eye but clear and well defined to his keen sense of smell - the after-images of creatures that hurried and scurried about their nocturnal business.

Abruptly he'll stop in his tracks, brought up sharply as if his very nose had been seized and held firmly. A scent, strangely familiar yet so strong, that it overpowers all others, assails his senses. The old dog fox has recently passed that way.

I can still remember the scent of his father which long ago had caused me to pause and ponder in those same fields which had been my playground.

A gentle slope rises gradually to where a wall of trees marks the edge of a small wood. It crowns the low rise and, as he approaches, his presence disturbs occasional rabbits that dare to venture out in daylight from the protective cover of the trees. He cannot resist chasing the bobbing white tails that scurry back to the sanctuary of briar and burrow. He'll never catch them though, just as I never could! They're too fast, and anyway, it's just an irresistible urge (not a real need) that compels him to try.

As he passes between the great beeches that stand like sentinels guarding the wood's perimeter, the ground below his feet changes abruptly from dew-damp grass to moist earth. The leaf-litter of centuries, still bearing the desiccated remnants of last autumn's fall, crunches and rustles beneath his paws.

The feel of the wood, so different from that of the field, heightens his senses and he revels in the proximity of so many trees. They rise above him, their great limbs dividing again and again, a lattice-work of bough and branch, their terminal twigs forming a canopy of filigree that sways with creaks and groans in the morning breeze. Here too are different smells - the many residual signatures of woodland creatures. Most common are those of squirrels that chase and scold each other above his head. How they used to frustrate me, those wretched tree rats! They venture down in search of winter hoards, but like the rabbits scurry away as you approach, their gossamer tails seeming to float behind them as they scamper back to the safety of the trees. Of course he gives chase - he cannot help himself - then, just as he thinks he has one in his grasp, just as he's sure that his teeth will close on its elusive little form, it vanishes from sight behind a tree. Looking up he spots his quarry, tantalizingly close, sitting in the fork of a branch just above his head. He barks wildly and circles the trunk, shattering the peace with yelps of anger and frustration while the squirrel looks down from above, apparently taunting this stupid noisy creature that has invaded its woodland territory. Then master will call him on and reluctantly he'll follow.

At the centre of the wood the trees thin out and an open glade breaks the cover of branch and twig. Grass returns under foot and it's here that the badgers have their set. For generations they have lived here - below ground in the day, and only venturing out as dusk falls. The young dog runs between the black holes with excitement and curiosity, his nose explores the pungent aroma of creatures he may never meet - the set's latrine - mounds of discarded bedding that one of the old sows has expelled and replaced the previous night and deep scratches on the silver white bark of a birch that fringes the glade. His nose interprets the ongoing saga of this subterranean community, which he reads like a book. Nowhere are these stronger than the ones rising from the dark tunnels, whose diameters are just too small to permit him access.

Then on again to the far side of the wood. An old cart-track marks the boundary of trees and the resumption of open fields. This ancient road skirts the woodland. In places it has become sunken with the passage of wheels and feet. In spring the high banks bear an explosion of colour. Countless wild flowers burst forth as the year matures and the days lengthen and grow warmer.

I remember the profusion of scents from their blossoms that drew countless tiny insects, hissing and buzzing to drink nectar from their hidden depths - a cunning lure to dust their minuscule bodies with pollen - nature's design to ensure next season's regeneration.

And so back, along the track to where it finally meets the lane. It emerges just below the entrance to the fields, then past the old stump back to the garden gate.

Here I still lie, waiting patiently. I rise stiffly to welcome my master's return. He pats me absent - mindedly as he passes. The young dog and I exchange glances as he enters the house, a superior smug expression on his face. I pay no heed as I settle down on the step once more. I look out to the fields beyond the garden and smile to myself.

You see, one day, when I am gone and just a distant memory to him - when his muzzle is white and his body heavy - when his legs will carry him only as far as the garden gate, he will lie here as I do now - in retirement. He'll watch as master leads another young dog away and in his mind he'll follow, remembering the fields and woods of his youth.

Stable Mates

Allow me to introduce myself. My name is Winston; Winston Churchill of Strathblair to be precise and I'm a Black Labrador.

My name - Winston Churchill - as I understand, it was the name of a very famous man connected to the aristocracy. It is, therefore, an appropriate name for a dog of my quality and breeding. However, you can call me Winston.

Everybody calls me Winston, with the exception of Jackson.
Jackson, my friend and partner, is a Springer Spaniel. Like Springer Spaniels in general, he's a fine working dog - but, like Springer Spaniels in general, it has to be said that he's rather uncouth.

I don't like to be disparaging about my friend, but I'm sure you'll understand what I mean.

Jackson, you see, has a rather carefree attitude to life. He doesn't seem to have the same regard for demeanour that I, as a Labrador, consider essential. You only have to watch him at work. I'm the first to admit that, when in the field, he performs his duties with great efficiency. Sadly, his bearing and deportment leave a great deal to be desired. He has a tendency to charge about wildly. He'll quarter a field or an entire hillside, backwards and forwards, nothing seems to bar his way, neither briar or thicket. No matter how dense the undergrowth may be, Jackson simply ploughs straight through. Indeed, I actually believe that the greater the challenge an obstacle presents him, the more determined he is to conquer it. His energy seems to know no bounds, a veritable dynamo of focused concentration, and therein lies the problem. Jackson has no regard for appearances - something we Labradors believe holds great importance. The way he gallivants about, covered in mud and pieces of undergrowth, tongue lolling from the side of his mouth, is really very undignified.

Still, Jackson is a splendid fellow for all his faults - a typical Springer Spaniel.

Oh yes, Winnie! That's what he insists on calling me. Makes me sound like a damned horse. I really do dislike it. I don't hold with abbreviated or nick names (as Jackson calls them) and cringe every time he uses it, especially if we're in company. Still that's Jackson for you.

All things considered he's not a bad chap - as Springers go that is - and he is my best friend, so I would appreciate it if you didn't mention any of the things that I've just said about him. It would be rather bad form don't you know and I'm not sure he'd understand. We do have to share a kennel after all!

Hi! My name's Jack. Actually my full name is Jackson, but I'm sure Winnie will have told you that. Jackson something of somewhere I can't remember. The master calls me "Jack the lad" I like that a lot, but Jack will do just fine.

Now I know that you've already spoken to my mate Winnie about me and I'm sure he's told you how rough and ready I am, but that's Winnie for you. Just between you and me, dear old Winnie's a bit of a snob. Maybe I am a bit rough and ready, but I enjoy life. Where's the harm in that? Life's too short to worry about what other dogs think of me.

To Winnie appearance is everything. When he's out working in the field, instead of getting stuck in, like I do, he just sits by the master's side waiting for instructions. I can't understand it. Don't get me wrong - when the chips are down Winnie's the best retriever I've ever met. I've seen him fetch birds that nobody even knew were there, but you should hear the fuss he makes if he gets a bit muddy in the process. Water's the best though. If he has to retrieve a bird from water his face is a picture of disgust and irritation. The thought of his lovely black, shiny coat dripping wet and all spiky, really offends his sensibilities. "So undignified" he grumbles. Mind you, it never stops him. He doesn't hesitate for a second. Straight in he goes with a splash. However, it has to be said that I've never seen another dog leap into water with Winnie's poise and composure. I once asked him why, if he hated getting wet so much, did he do it so readily and so well? He answered by giving me one of his lectures about good breeding, first class training and always keeping a stiff upper lip in adversity. To be honest, I wish I hadn't asked.

I actually think Winnie's a bit of a fraud. On more than one occasion I've caught the expression on his face as he's leapt from the bank of a river or pond. It's one of almost puppy-like delight and there's a fiery gleam in his eye as he sails through the air.

Then there's the way he looks down his nose at other dogs. To hear him go on about other breeds you would think they were the scum of the earth. When he launches into one of his monologues on the superior qualities of Black Labradors I tend to switch off and go to sleep, or suddenly remember a little job that I'd been meaning to do. Anything other than having to listen to Winnie spout. I sometimes wonder what he really thinks of me.

Deep down I know he's a nice chap with a heart of gold, bless him! Most of his bluster is just hot air. His father was even worse and I suppose that, inevitably, some of it is bound to have rubbed off on him. What I do know for sure is that, if ever push came to shove, Winnie would be there for me, as I would be for him. Sharing a kennel does that to dogs. However, there are limits, so do me a favour, don't say anything to Winnie about - well, you know - what I've just said about him. He'd probably launch into one of his lectures, God-forbid!

List of Plates

The Tales' End!